# PRINCIPLES
# OF ANIMAL BEHAVIOR

*Under the Editorship of H. Philip Zeigler*

# PRINCIPLES
# OF ANIMAL BEHAVIOR

William N. Tavolga

*American Museum of Natural History
and The City University of New York*

HARPER & ROW, PUBLISHERS
New York, Evanston, and London

PRINCIPLES OF ANIMAL BEHAVIOR
*Copyright © 1969 by William N. Tavolga*

*Library of Congress Catalog Card Number: 69-13748*

To T. C. Schneirla

# CONTENTS

# PREFACE

The purpose here is to summarize certain basic principles that underlie the science of animal behavior. Some of these principles are unique and some are common to all of biology. Behavior is a manifestation of the structure and function of an animal, and, therefore, should be subject to rigorous analysis and experiment, based upon objective data. Mysticism, superstition, and uncritical anecdotes have no more place in the study of animal behavior than in any other branch of science. Unfortunately, the history of animal behavior has been, and is today, influenced by much nonscientific thinking. However, as a result of the multiple efforts of scientists in disciplines as diverse as genetics, ecology, psychology, physics, and developmental biology, a theoretical framework and a factual foundation for the study of animal behavior are beginning to emerge. It is this framework that I shall try to present here.

In recent years, there has been a strong increase in public and scientific interest in animal behavior, as witnessed by the establishment of many college courses in the field, a large new scientific society, and numerous publications. Recent textbooks on animal behavior have run the gamut from attempts at a comprehensive coverage to collections of reprinted articles. Comparisons among different organisms are commonly made, e.g., ant and human societies, bird and amphibian sound communication, and learning in fish and mammals. Similarities are usually stressed in such comparisons.

If one emphasizes the differences in such comparative studies, especially differences based upon levels of organization, it becomes evident that many similarities turn out to be only superficial resemblances. The newer trend, therefore, among both psychologists and biologists who study animal behavior has been a search for the developmental basis for these differences.

In searching for a unifying principle in animal behavior study, many have held to the idea of a dichotomy between innate and learned behavior, also variously termed: instinctive vs. learned; inherited vs. acquired; and phylogenetically acquired vs. individually acquired. Such a dichotomy is unreal, and adherence to it has resulted in much wasted effort in arguments in semantics and experiments designed to demonstrate rather than to test the hypothesis. A developmental view of behavior is not only consonant with the current advances in genetics and embryology, but renders the nature vs. nurture dichotomy useless.

The developmental approach to the study of animal behavior is not a simple one, and requires a considerable depth of experience and understanding to appreciate. However, biological principles are seldom simple. In the past, a substantial resistance to the acceptance of evolutionary concepts occurred because the operations of natural selection and its genetic effects are extremely complex, especially as compared to the naive Lamarckian idea of use and disuse.

In this small volume, no attempt is made to be comprehensive. Such treatments are available elsewhere. The purpose is to present a number of principles that currently guide many investigators in this field. Central to these principles is the concept of a developmental study of animal behavior.

A forerunner and major contributor to this concept has been T. C. Schneirla, of the American Museum of Natural History in New York. Spanning a highly productive period of over forty years, his papers and books have had a profound impact upon the field. Many of his former students and associates have gone on to become leaders in their own right. It is with some humility, therefore, that I should like to dedicate this book to Theodore C. Schneirla, my good friend and a continuing source of scientific inspiration.

I am grateful to Lester R. Aronson, James W. Atz, David W. Jacobs, Ethel Tobach, and H. Philip Zeigler for their comments and suggestions on the manuscript, and I thank my wife, Margaret C. Tavolga, for her patience in catching my grammatical errors. My thanks also to the many students who put up with my trying out various sections of this book in my lectures, and to the several who read and commented on the manuscript.

William N. Tavolga

*Postscript added in proof:*
    Dr. T. C. Schneirla died in August of 1968. His passing leaves a major hiatus in the field, and my own intellectual debts to him are beyond words.

# PRINCIPLES
# OF ANIMAL BEHAVIOR

# 1   INTRODUCTION

It is common to see a man walk into a restaurant, order a meal, and proceed to eat it. He manipulates his food with a variety of utensils, puts it into his mouth, manipulates it further with his teeth and tongue, and, finally, swallows it. To analyze this behavior, one has to examine it at several levels of complexity and organization. What are the visual, olfactory, gustatory, and tactual cues that this hungry man uses to select the food and, indeed, the restaurant? On another level, what are the internal physiological factors that lead him into and guide him through this behavior pattern? On still another level of organization, what are the psychological influences of his prior experience, his cultural background, his childhood memories, and even his political inclinations? Obviously, just observing this man eat does not give any satisfactory answers to such questions. A considerable number of experimental studies would be required of this man's behavior and that of many other men like him to determine the factors controlling this specific activity.

Perhaps it would be helpful to examine similar behavior in simpler organisms such as a frog. A frog feeds on insects by lunging the body forward, simultaneously opening the mouth and flicking the tongue toward

1

FIG. 1.    Feeding behavior of a frog.

the prey. The tongue is attached at the front of the lower jaw and is covered by a sticky mucus to which the prey adheres. The tongue is then retracted into the mouth and the prey swallowed. (See Fig. 1.) Observation of this behavior shows clearly that if the prey is immobile, there is no feeding lunge on the part of the frog, whereas almost any small object moving at the right speed and at the correct distance will evoke a feeding response. Experimental analyses of this behavior in conjunction with anatomical and physiological studies of the frog's eye show that the retina is, in a sense, a "bug detector." The eye, therefore, sends a simple "go" or "no-go" message to the brain. It does not respond to visual stimuli in the frog's environment in this manner unless the stimulus consists of a small, moving object at the right distance. In the frog's normal habitat, this "go" stimulus is very likely to be a moving insect, and, thus the frog's behavior is efficiently adapted for surviving in a particular environment. We can see here how specialization in a sense organ can, in a way, regulate and determine a behavior.

Within the first day of hatching from its egg, a baby chick begins to feed efficiently by pecking at small particles of food on the ground, but there is a development of this behavior during these first hours. At first the pecking simply consists of a quick lunge of the head, but gradually the eyes guide the orientation of the lunge, and the animal begins to peck at specific objects. Eventually, the chick synchronizes and organizes all the various sense organs and motor responses and the random pecking develops into a smooth and efficient feeding behavior. The development of this pecking behavior can probably be traced back to a time when the chick is still inside the egg as shown in Fig. 2. In a 48-hour old chick embryo, the heart is a very large bulging organ, and the head is bent so that it is in contact with the steadily beating heart. The beating of the heart tends to make the head bob up and down. At this stage, the musculature of the neck and trunk is beginning to differentiate. After about five or six days of incubation, the muscles of the neck develop to the point at which they are able to control the movements of the head, and the bobbing motion, initiated by the heartbeat, is taken over by these muscles. At ten days of age, the embryo is quite motile and exhibits head, wing, leg, and body movements. It is probable, therefore, that the pecking behavior has its origins in the early embryo, and what began as a passive movement, involving only the organs directly concerned, develops into a complex series of actions integrated by the central nervous system. The point at which we might call the behavior "pecking" is really arbitrary and a matter of convenience. What is more important is the idea that behavior develops from primordia just as structure does.

If a small particle of food touches a single tentacle of a sea anemone, only that one tentacle responds at first. A sea anemone, a member of the phylum Coelenterata (or Cnidaria, according to some authors), is a simple, two-layered, radially symmetrical animal with a nervous system consisting of a network of interconnecting neurons. Cells sensitive to touch and to certain chemicals respond to contact by releasing stinging and holding threads (nematocysts), and contractile cells in the immediate area shorten. As a result, the food particle is caught and held, and the tentacle involved begins to contract and pull the food toward the mouth. By means of a slow spread of the stimulus to the rest of the animal, via the nerve network, all the tentacles may become involved in surrounding the prey and drawing it toward the mouth (Fig. 3). This illustrates feeding behavior in an animal at a very low level of organization, and shows how an animal without a central nervous system can perform some coordinated activities.

The above examples illustrate some very different kinds of feeding behavior, but, more significantly, they illustrate the kinds of questions a student of animal behavior is likely to ask. Given an animal doing something, the observer will, of course, first describe and define the behavior,

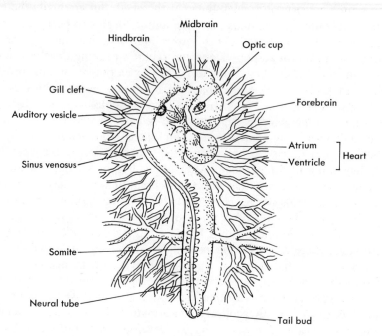

(A)

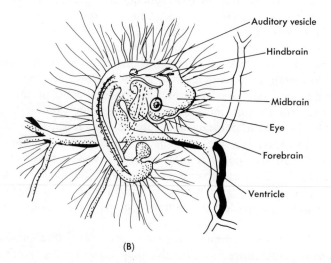

(B)

FIG. 2.    Development of the chick. (A) Embryo after 48 hours. (B) Embryo after 96 hours.

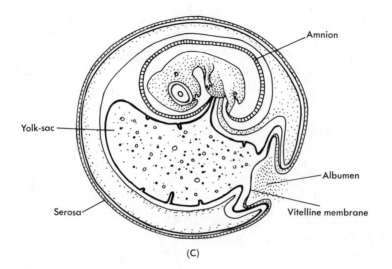

(C)

(D)

(C) 10-day-old embryo in membranes. (D) Chick after hatching, about 21 days. ((A), (B), and (C) based on Bradley M. Patten, *Foundations of Embryology*, 2nd ed., copyright © 1964 by McGraw Hill Book Company.)

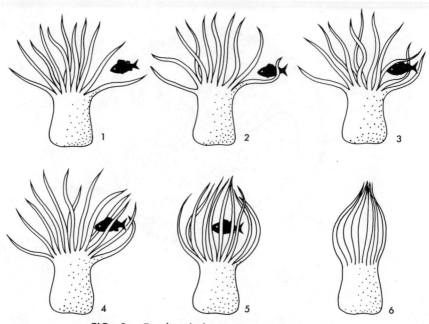

FIG. 3.  Feeding behavior in a coelenterate.

but he will then ask what are the sensory cues from the environment that stimulate this behavior? How does the structure and function of the sense organs control the information delivered to the integrating centers? How does the behavior develop, i.e., what are the environmental factors, the internal conditions, the effects of past experience, the hereditary influences that determine that the behavior should develop in a particular way under particular circumstances? How do all these influences operate together as the animal matures? How does the behavior in question affect the survival of the animal and the survival of the species? It is also apparent that organisms at different branches of the phylogenetic tree differ qualitatively in the mechanisms involved in doing the same thing, as, for example, the mechanisms of feeding. The student of behavior, therefore, is also interested in the evolutionary origins of behavior and the relationships among the organisms he studies.

## Suggested Readings

Kuo, Z. Y. 1967. *The Dynamics of Behavioral Development: An Epigenetic View*. Random House: New York.

McGill, T. E. (ed.). 1965. *Readings in Animal Behavior*. Holt, Rinehart and Winston: New York.

Maier, N. R. F., and T. C. Schneirla. 1935. *Principles of Animal Psychology*. Enlarged ed. 1964. Dover Publications: New York.

Marler, P., and W. J. Hamilton. 1966. *Mechanisms of Animal Behavior*. John Wiley & Sons: New York.

Maturana, H. R., J. Y. Lettvin, W. S. McCulloch, and W. H. Pitts. 1960. Anatomy and physiology of vision in the frog (*Rana pipiens*). *J. Gen. Physiol.*, 43: 129–175.

# 2  FUNDAMENTALS

Man thinks of himself as a superior being on this planet, and he is always amazed when other animals behave in a manner appropriate to any given environmental situation. Our attention is caught by the unusual. We marvel at the ability of bees to communicate to their hive mates the location of a food source. We are awed when a bird navigates over miles of open sea with no compass or charts. We admire the spider who needs no engineering courses to construct a beautiful and efficiently suspended web. A closer look, however, shows us that all the living organisms on this planet, including ourselves, perform complex activities that arise from a basic property of cytoplasmic life: *irritability*, i.e., the ability to respond to changes in the environment. Unlike the response of an inanimate object to an external force, the reaction of a living organism is generally *adaptive*. This means that the probability of the survival of the species is increased because the animal can adjust its response so that it is appropriate to the changing conditions.

Whatever an animal does is a complex result of its skeletal and muscular equipment, its sensory input, its physiological state, its developmental experience, its genetic background, and many other factors. When we ask how an organism responds to its environment, how this response aids

8

species survival, and how these activities become formed into the total *species-typical* behavior pattern, we have begun our study of animal behavior. When we get over our initial, naive wonder at Nature's works, and get down to controlled observation and measurement, we have taken our first step into animal behavior as a science.

### SOME MILESTONES IN THE HISTORY OF ANIMAL BEHAVIOR

Throughout the history of man, there has always been an interest in what other animals do and a curiosity about why they do it. Prehistoric man had a practical stake in lore about the animals he hunted. The ancient caveman's paintings emphasized animals, and the arrows that pointed to vital parts might well have been the first "chalk talks" by some ancient lecturer in a course on how to hunt and how to predict what the hunted animal is likely to do when attacked. When man first started to domesticate animals, he must have observed the behavior of his primitive dogs and cattle.

Centuries later, the cosmologically minded Greek philosophers wrote about animal behavior. Although most of the behavioral ideas of these early scientists were concerned with the principles of soul, mind, love, hate, and other abstractions, Aristotle in his *Historia Animalium* discussed locomotion, mating, parental behavior, and many other aspects of animal behavior. Some of his material was from personal observation, but most was based upon anecdotes of others, with a strong admixture of his own preconceived notions. The result is a work in which careful and detailed naturalistic observations alternate with anecdotes of dubious authenticity and ingenious reasoning. Aristotle's description of the behavior of bees is a detailed and remarkably accurate one, yet in the midst of this description one finds the following passage:

> Wax is made from flowers. They bring the material of wax from the droppings of trees, but the honey falls from the air, principally about the rising of the stars and when the rainbow rests upon the earth. . . . We argue that wax is made from flowers but that bees do not make honey, but simply collect that which falls; for those who keep bees find the cells filled with honey in the course of one or two days. In the autumn, there are flowers enough but the bees make no honey if that which they produced is taken away. But if one supply were taken away and they were in want of food, they would make more, if they procured it from flowers. (*Historia Animalium,* Book V, ch. XIX, 4)

Equally typical is:

> When eagles grow old, their beaks become more and more curved so that at last they die of starvation. The story goes that the eagle was once a man and suffers this as punishment for inhospitality to a guest. (*Ibid.*, Book IX, ch. XXII, p. 4)

Aristotle's writings contain traces of many modern ideas, but they also lack factual, confirmable data. This weakness was generally true of most pre-Renaissance science.

Lack of data, however, was not one of Charles Darwin's weaknesses. In the great mass of facts he accumulated lay the strength of his theory of evolution. He was concerned with the morphological (i.e., structural) evolution of man, and he also attempted to explain the evolution of man's mentality. Thinking of evolution as a continuum, he proposed that the behavioral differences between man and other animals were purely quantitative. Both possess the same emotions, instincts, memories, and other mental properties, but to different degrees. Unfortunately, his data were often mixed with anecdotal evidence and unquantified observations. In spite of what we would now consider its weaknesses, Darwin's contribution to animal behavior was highly significant, and the science of comparative psychology began with the publication of Darwin's books, especially, *The Expression of the Emotions in Man and Animals* (1872). Figure 4 shows a chimpanzee described as "disappointed and sulky." Actually, the description is based upon how one would expect a human being to feel under comparable circumstances. Although anthropomorphic, this was one of the earliest attempts to make objective comparisons of behavior between man and other animals and to seek features in common.

In 1894, C. Lloyd Morgan, in one of the first books on comparative psychology, enunciated a principle that has become axiomatic in the study of animal behavior: "In no case may we interpret an action as the outcome of the exercise of a higher psychical faculty, if it can be interpreted as the outcome of the exercise of one which stands lower in the psychological scale."

A classic example of the application of this principle in the study of animal behavior is the case of Clever Hans, a trained horse whose apparently phenomenal intelligence aroused considerable interest in both lay and scientific circles shortly after the turn of the century. The following account of the case is excerpted from John B. Watson's text *Behavior, An Introduction to Comparative Psychology*.

> At the height of his career Hans showed the following scientific accomplishments . . . : he had mastered the cardinal numbers from 1 to 100 and the ordinals to 10. Upon request he would count objects

FIG. 4.   Chimpanzee from *The Expression of the Emotions in Man and Animals* by Darwin.

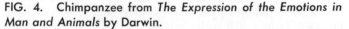

of all sorts, the persons present, even to distinctions of sex; then hats, umbrellas, and eyeglasses. All forms of simple arithmetical problems involving addition, subtraction, multiplication, and division. He could do fractions, changing them first into decimals. E.g., "How much is 2/5 + 1/2?" Answer, 9/10 (tapping first the numerator and then the denominator). Or again: "I have a number in mind. I subtract 9 and have 3 as a remainder. What is the number?" (12). "What are the factors of 28?" Whereupon Hans taps consecutively 2, 4, 7, 14, 28. He was able to read German readily, whether written or printed. If a series of placards with written words was placed before the horse he would step up and point with his nose to any of the words required of him. With his alphabet he would answer simple questions, e.g.: "What is the woman holding in her hand?" Hans spelled without hesitation "Schirm" (parasol). Furthermore, his memory was excellent. He carried the entire yearly calendar in his head. He could give not only the date of each day without having been previously taught, but also the date of any day one might mention. He could tell the time to the minute.

A scientific commission was finally established to investigate the horse. By a series of careful tests, Pfungst, a psychologist, was able to show that Hans' behavior was actually based upon a very simple level of behavioral function. Watson's account of the analysis follows.

> Hans could not read, calculate, or count unless some one present knew the answers. Pfungst established this, indeed, beyond even a doubt by putting a series of questions to the horse, the answers to which were not known to the questioner. A card containing a certain number was picked at random by the experimenter and exhibited to the horse in such a way that no one could see it (the answer being unknown to the experimeter himself). When tested in this way, procedure without knowledge, the horse returned only 8% of correct responses, whereas he responded with an accuracy of 98% in those cases where the questioner knew the answers.
>
> . . .
>
> Carrying the analysis one step farther, Pfungst found that vision was necessary for correct response. When the horse was perfectly blinded almost no correct responses could be obtained (only 6% were correct). The final link in unraveling the "mystery" came when Pfungst discovered the signs by means of which the horse responded. These signals were the minimal movements of the questioner's head. "As soon as the experimenter had given a problem to the horse, he involuntarily bent his head and trunk slightly forward and the horse would then put his right foot forward and begin to tap, without, however, returning it to its original position. As soon as the desired number of taps were given, the questioner would make a slight upward jerk of his head. Thereupon the horse would immediately swing his foot in a wide circle, bringing it back to the original position. (This movement which, in the following exposition we shall designate as "the back step," was never included in the count.) Now after Hans had ceased tapping the questioner would raise his head and trunk to their normal position. This second, far coarser movement, was not the signal for the back step, but always followed it. But whenever this second movement was omitted, Hans, who had already brought back his foot to the original position and had thereby put it out of commission, as it were, would give one more tap with his left foot." These minimal movements turned out to be exceedingly small (1/5 mm. and upward). If this analysis of Pfungst's is correct the responses of Hans are exactly similar to those with which we have long been familiar in the laboratory.

The application of Morgan's canon to psychology accomplished two major advances: the beginning of the elimination of anthropomorphism, i.e., the endowment of animals with human characteristics, and the strengthening of the concept of levels of behavioral organizations.

The psychologists of Darwin's period were primarily concerned with the concepts of "mind" and "consciousness." They belonged to what has

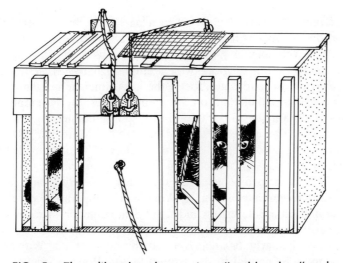

FIG. 5. Thorndike placed a cat in a "problem box" such that the cat could open the latch and get to its bowl of milk by stepping on a treadle and pulling a string. Initially, the cat's movements were not directed at the treadle, but by chance the treadle was pressed. Thereafter, through a series of successive trials, the treadle gradually became the center of attention and other, nonrewarding, movements became fewer. Eventually, the cat learned to press the treadle and open the latch. (After Edward L. Thorndike, *Animal Intelligence,* The Macmillan Co., 1911.)

been termed the school of "introspection." Virtually all judgments and interpretations were made on the basis of the observers' own feelings and subjective impressions. A major break with this introspective school was made by E. L. Thorndike, who established certain principles that had a profound influence on experimental psychology.

One of Thorndike's most important contributions was his "Law of Effect." This law states that responses followed by some reward or source of satisfaction to the animal will tend to become associated with that reward, and, by contrast, any noxious or unpleasant stimulus will tend to inhibit a behavioral response with which it is associated. A modified form of this law is the basis for much of the work on conditioning and experimental learning that is going on even today. Thorndike devised a "problem box," such as that shown in Fig. 5, in which cats, dogs and other animals were faced with the problem of opening a door to obtain food or to escape, and attempted to measure the relative intelligence of various species by this method. The problem box was later modified into a "discrimination box," in which animals were trained to select a particular door or compartment.

Thorndike's work directly influenced the subsequent development of comparative psychology in America. The "problem box" was the forerunner of many testing devices which emphasize the *objective* study of animal behavior. Such devices focus the experimenter's attention on the animal's *responses* rather than on his mental states. By its emphasis upon the automatic "stamping in" or stimulus–response connections, the Law of Effect reinforced this tendency toward objectivity. Moreover, although the early comparative psychologists studied a wide variety of animal behaviors, such breadth of interest soon became the exception rather than the rule. Thorndike's work helped to establish the study of learning and motivation as the central research problem of American comparative psychology to the exclusion of other interesting and significant behavioral processes.

The early twentieth century saw the formation of many "schools" of psychology, particularly *behaviorism,* attributed to J. B. Watson, whose ideas were most influential in the United States. Watson virtually rejected the idea of inheritance of behavior, and at the same time adhered strongly to the objectivism of Morgan and Thorndike. Watson's influence, like that of Thorndike, resulted in a strong trend among American experimental psychologists toward a study of learning as the basis of behavior.

A major contribution to the study of animal behavior came from the physiologists, especially those concerned with the mechanisms of the nervous system and its relation to behavior. The concept of a *reflex* as an automatic, simple response to a stimulus was developed. Indeed, some physiologists proposed that *all* behavior could be explained on the basis of interacting, interdependent reflexes.

I. P. Pavlov, the great Russian physiologist, presented a dog with two stimuli in succession: the ringing of a bell and the presentation of food. At first, the dog responded only to the presentation of food by an increase in salivary flow. After many repetitions of this pair of stimuli, the dog's salivary flow was increased upon the ringing of the bell alone. The experiment was carefully controlled by keeping the animal in an observation chamber with the experimenter so placed that he could observe without becoming part of the stimulus (see Fig. 6). Thus, Pavlov developed the concept of a *conditioned reflex* and showed how simple, unitary actions could be associated with specific stimuli by contiguity in time.

The development of the science of animal behavior includes many other major contributors in addition to Darwin, Morgan, Thorndike, Pavlov, and Watson. The sequence, however, illustrates an important basic change in the science. No longer can one assume some sort of human mind in the body of an animal; the behavior of each species is to be investigated on its own terms. Techniques of observation and experiment must be

(A) (B)

FIG. 6. Conditioned reflex experiment of Pavlov. (A) Experimenter's section of the double chamber. (B) Animal's section of the double chamber. (After Ivan P. Pavlov, *Conditioned Reflexes*, (G.V. Anrep, trans. & ed.), 1927. Clarendon Press, Oxford.)

adapted to the behavioral capacities of the given species. Furthermore, objective observations and controlled experiments must be relied upon, rather than sporadic, second-hand anecdotes.

In the 1930's, Konrad Z. Lorenz began a series of publications which came to establish a European school of animal behavior called *ethology*. Lorenz revived certain ideas of earlier naturalists and presented a theory of instinctive behavior based largely upon the concept of inheritance of behavior. In part, this theory was a reaction to American researchers' emphasis on learning and the extensive use of the laboratory rat in their work. He and his co-workers, notably N. Tinbergen, conceived of innate (inherited; instinctive) behavior as the result of the activity of certain hierarchically arranged centers in the nervous system. In his study of mating behavior in the stickleback, Tinbergen found that the members of a pair go through a series of stereotyped behavior patterns. These patterns occur in sequence, so that a given behavior by the male will stimulate the female to perform some activity, and this in turn stimulates the male, and so on. Each action is a stimulus for the next action and yet depends on the previous action (see Fig. 7).

The ethologists have emphasized the study of animals under natural conditions and have devoted most of their attention to species-typical behavior. The activity and the enthusiasm of many of the ethologists have

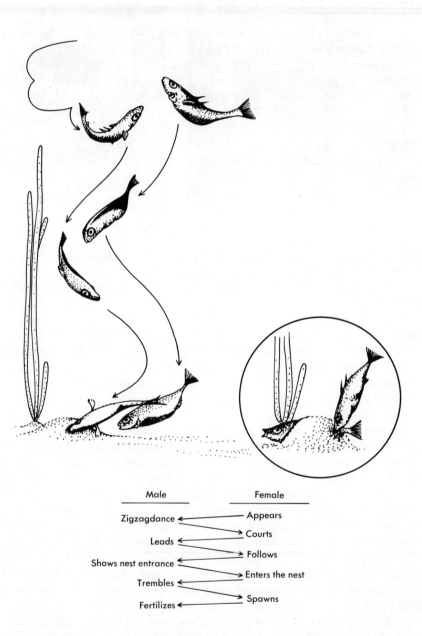

| Male | Female |
|---|---|
| Zigzagdance ← | → Appears |
| Leads ← | → Courts |
| Shows nest entrance ← | → Follows |
| Trembles ← | → Enters the nest |
| Fertilizes ← | → Spawns |

FIG. 7. The mating behavior in the stickleback. (After N. Tinbergen, *The Study of Instinct*, Oxford University Press, 1951.)

stimulated much interest in the investigation of a wide variety of animals and their behavioral adaptations.

At present, the original school of ethology or instinct theory has become diffused, and the term "ethology" has become virtually a synonym for the study of animal behavior. Lorenz, however, represents a significant branch in the development of the science, in that the importance of naturalistic studies was brought out by his work. Unfortunately, this resurgence was accompanied by a revival of the nature *vs.* nurture controversy.

Most modern investigators tend to accept a less rigid distinction between the innate and the acquired. They find it is more fruitful to investigate the mechanisms that control and evoke the behavior, rather than to make a priori assumptions about the genetic or environmental contributions. This point will be developed later.

## COMPARATIVE PSYCHOLOGY
## AND ANIMAL BEHAVIOR

In the early nineteenth century, *comparative anatomy* meant simply the study of various animal parts to find similarities and differences in structure. With the advent of evolutionary concepts, comparative anatomy became closely involved in the study of evolution. Comparisons of living animals with fossil forms were particularly valuable to elucidate evolutionary trends and changes. Thus, the family tree, i.e., *phylogeny,* of a species can be reconstructed. The concept of *homology* arose with comparative anatomy. Homology is the idea that two structures in different species that look different and serve different functions may have arisen from a common ancestral structure and thus show similarities in embryonic development and basic organization. Thus, the human arm, the bird's wing, and the pectoral fin of a fish are homologous structures. A less evident but equally valid homologous relationship is that between the mammalian middle ear bones and certain jaw elements in sharks.

Our present use of the term "comparative" carries with it all the implications of phylogeny and homology inherent in the principles of evolution, and the same implications are present in the field of *comparative psychology.*

One of the major problems in comparative behavior study is that of homology. In morphology, fossil evidence is almost essential in the reconstruction of phylogeny, but, unfortunately, behavior leaves little or no record in the rocks. Thus, when an observer sees behavioral similarities among organisms, his inferences about evolutionary development and relationships must remain pure hypotheses except when supported by evidence derived from morphological homology.

(A)

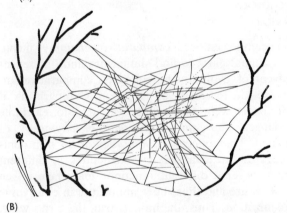

(B)

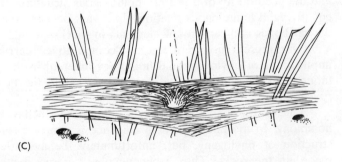

(C)

FIG. 8.   Different types of spider webs. (A) orb weaver web; (B) irregular network; (C) flat, nonsticky web.

A case in point is the classification of spiders. Many of the major groups are quite difficult to separate on the basis of structure alone, especially when the characteristic differentiating structures are present only in males. On the basis of behavior, however, these groups are readily and consistently separable. The particular behavior studied is the construction of a web, and the type of web immediately characterizes the group and, sometimes, the species, although some families of spiders never construct food-catching webs. (See Fig. 8.) This behavioral comparison, however, tells us little or nothing about the evolution of web-building. We can construct elaborate diagrams showing the relationships of spiders, but without fossil (i.e., historical) data, no one can ascertain what web structure is primitive.

These difficulties, however, should not discourage comparative behavioral studies, because, in many cases, such investigations have assisted in demonstrating evolutionary relationships. This is particularly true when comparing closely related forms, such as species within a genus or family. In some cases, as with the classification of spiders, behavior is important for the study of taxonomy and phylogeny. For these purposes, it must be presumed that the animals not only have a species-typical constitution but have developed in a species-typical environment.

### THE PRINCIPLE OF LEVELS IN THE STUDY OF ANIMAL BEHAVIOR

Throughout our world, organization exists at many levels. Atoms are organized into molecules; elements into compounds; purine and pyrimidine bases into nucleic acids; cells into tissues; tissues into organs; and, often, individual animals are organized into social systems or civilizations. Scientific investigation usually attempts to understand these levels of organization, either by description or by experimentation.

When a protein is hydrolyzed to its component amino acids, we are no longer able to determine the properties of the protein by testing the properties of the amino acids. We cannot describe the architecture of a house by analyzing or by counting the pieces of wood and the bricks. The properties of the protein, like the architecture of the house, are based upon the way in which the pieces are put together, that is, how they are *organized*. Thus, the whole is greater than the sum of its parts, in the sense that it has acquired new properties, new features, and new functions not present in any of the individual parts. Organization is particularly complex and difficult to comprehend in biological systems.

The study of each level of organization has its own specializations, and, indeed, its own hypotheses and theories, and the same methods of study are, at best, applicable only to closely related levels. Knowledge of the physiology of nerve conduction, for example, can be directly applied to the study of the polarization of cell membranes, or to the functioning of simple neuron networks, but it is of only limited help in interpreting the mechanisms of schizophrenia. The latter represents an interaction of all parts of the organism with its environment and past history and is the result of a change in the organization. We must be cautious in drawing conclusions about one level of organization from information acquired at another level.

Unfortunately, the same words are often used to describe similar situations at different levels. Organic evolution is adaptive, but natural selection operating on a gene pool is not purposeful in the sense of anticipated goal-seeking. Yet the words "evolution" and "mutation" are commonly used in describing cultural changes in human history. Cultural evolution is manifestly different in its mechanisms, in its processes, and, most important, in the *level of organization* upon which it operates. Cultural evolution is uniquely human and results from the ability of man to communicate his ideas and abstractions to other men across both space and time. Thus, the changes that take place in human societies are qualitatively different from those of organic evolution. The resemblances between organic and cultural evolution are purely superficial, and the use of the same words to label these different phenomena often results in misconceptions, especially by the lay public.

Another example of confusion of levels is shown in the use of terms such as "memory," "learning," and "brain" in computer technology. Science fiction writers have made much of "intelligent" machines, and the layman often has fears of automation and of emotionless robots controlling his life. The human mind and the machine operate on very different levels of organization, and the machine is only a mechanical extension of human communication. Storage of information by a computer is essentially the same as the printing in a book and is obviously different from the mechanism of human memory (which is as yet poorly understood). The use of the same words for superficially similar phenomena is a common occurrence in our language, but, as in this instance, such usage can lead not only to semantic confusion but also to a confusion of different levels of organization.

Often it is useful to make comparisons among phenomena at different levels, but the qualitative differences in organization must not be neglected.

Phylogeny, i.e., the study of evolutionary relationships, is also concerned with levels of evolutionary advance and specialization. A comparison of a cellular organization, as in the Protozoa, with that of multicellular animals shows that even the lowly *Hydra* or *Planaria* possesses integrative features that involve mechanisms different from any present in the protozoans. The differences between the radially symmetrical coelenterates and the bilaterally symmetrical flatworms include differences in organization, such as cephalization, and differentiated sense organs.

In the sense defined above, the different psychological levels, i.e., levels of behavioral organization, among animals are usually closely linked to the morphological levels. Consider the differences between two groups of animals representing the ends of two very different branches of the animal kingdom: insects and vertebrates. Insects (arthropods) have a ventral nervous system composed of connected solid ganglia, a chitinous exoskeleton, a segmented body pattern, an open circulatory system, and some characteristic sensory mechanisms, including compound eyes. Vertebrates (chordates) have a dorsal tubular nervous system, segmentation developed at a later stage and in an different manner, an endoskeleton of bone and cartilage, a closed circulatory system, many other characteristic differences. (See Fig. 9.) In behavior and behavioral development, the two groups are equally diverse. Insects possess an inflexible developmental pattern leading to a strongly stereotyped behavioral repertoire; the vertebrates, and especially the mammals, by contrast, show a more plastic behavioral complex. Without going into further detail at this point, it is clear that the two groups represent different levels of organization, and any attempt to interpret the behavior of an insect with concepts and methods based on human psychology would be as ridiculous as attempting a Freudian psychoanalysis of a cockroach.

In a causal analysis of behavior of a given species, it is necessary to recognize the level of organization (See Fig. 10) at which the analysis takes place. For example, let us select a particular behavior pattern—a man with hereditary baldness buys a toupee. Here a particular combination of genes appears to influence a behavior. One could even say that this man possesses a combination of bases in a DNA (deoxyribonucleic acid) chain that causes him to buy a wig. This is obviously nonsensical, but it demonstrates that it is inappropriate to explain a phenomenon at a given level of organization with data, concepts, and methods from another level. In this instance, the psychological and social factors of vanity, social conformity, and insecurity undoubtedly play a much more important and direct role in the determination of the behavior than do the physiological factors of endocrine balance and the remote effect of a gene mutation upon some enzyme system. Another aspect needs to be considered here. The man's baldness is a result of a lifetime of development: of the intricate interaction of his hereditary materials with both external and internal environmental processes and changes.

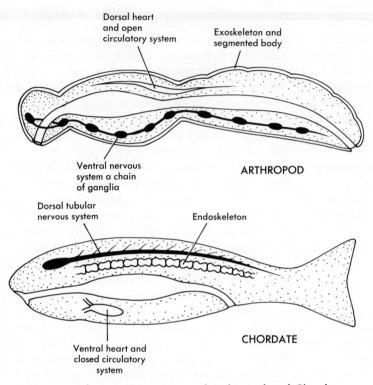

FIG. 9.   Schematic comparison of Arthropod and Chordate.

The phototactic behavior of a fly can be studied on a simpler level. In a beam of light, the intensity of the illumination on the two eyes affects the vigor of muscular contraction on the two sides of the body. When illumination is the same on both eyes, the animal is oriented into the beam and proceeds toward the light source. If illumination of one eye is decreased by either moving the beam or blinding one eye, the vigor of leg movements on the blind or shaded side is increased so that the animal turns toward the light as shown in Fig 11. Thus, we say that the animal is "attracted" toward the light. What has heredity to do with this behavior? It is clear that positive phototaxis is not directly built into the genes, but, rather, the particular combination of hereditary factors, i.e., DNA construction, results in the development of enzyme systems. These enzyme systems, when existing in an environment characteristic of the fly, channel the development of structural and functional systems. These, in turn, result in the development of this phototactic behavior. In contrast to the bald-headed man, the fly's behavior is quite stereotyped and unaffected by complex so-

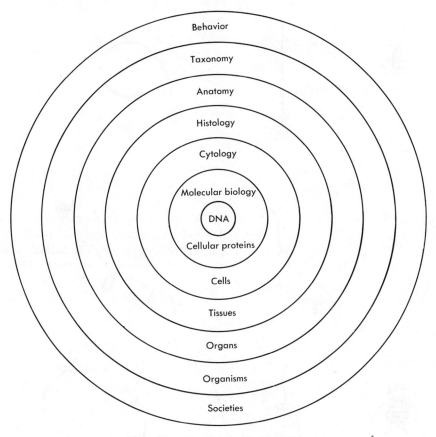

FIG. 10.    Levels of organization.

cial and cultural factors, but a biochemical analysis of the behavior is still not possible because of the many intervening levels of organization between the gene pattern and the overt behavior. We must still ask the question: How does the behavior develop?


ONTOGENETIC APPROACH
TO BEHAVIOR STUDY

The casual observer of animal behavior tends to classify activities into one of two categories: instinctive, i.e., innate and inherited, or learned through experience. This is an easy and tempting oversimplification and a trap for the unwary student. At the base of this dichotomy is the old

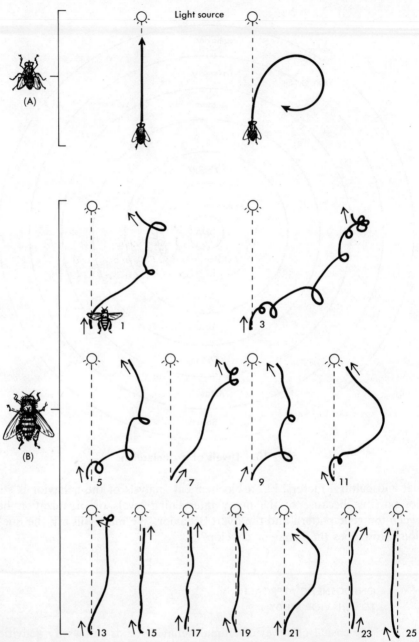

FIG. 11.    Phototaxis in fly (A) and bee (B), effect of blinding on one side. (B) shows the consecutive tracks of a bee with the left eye blackened, in directive light. The circus movements to the right in the first few tracks later gradually straighten and the animal eventually walks directly towards the light. ((B) after G.S. Fraenkel and D.L. Gunn, *The Orientation of Animals*, Dover Publications, 1961.)

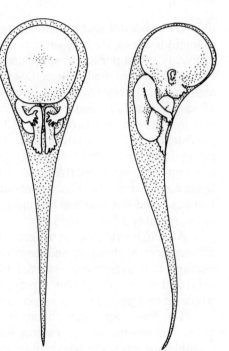

FIG. 12.   Seventeenth century conception of a sperm cell.

controversy of nature *vs.* nurture. How much of the behavior of a man, mouse, or fly is the result of inherited, unchangeable nature, and how much is conditioned by the environment in which it lives? On the surface, these appear to be logical, rational questions, but a careful study shows that they conceal an unproven assumption. This assumption is that inherited and acquired behavior are somehow clearly separable, and one can easily distinguish between them. In fact, the evidence of experiment and observation tends to deny such a clear-cut distinction, and we shall proceed to examine this question in further detail later. Casual observers are not the only ones caught in this trap. Many reputable scientists have supported the existence of this dichotomy, and have made a priori assumptions that certain behavior patterns are learned and others are innate.

Modern genetics and developmental biology have dealt primarily with structural characteristics, and we have long ago discarded the notions of seventeenth-century biologists, such as Leeuwenhoek, that the individual is completely preformed in the sperm or egg. (See Fig. 12.) The principle of epigenesis is now accepted; i.e., the organism develops from an undifferentiated mass of protoplasm—a single cell. Furthermore, it is clear that this primordial cell, the zygote, is not truly undifferentiated, but possesses specialized parts. At each stage of development, the organism goes through different structural and functional metamorphoses, each stage representing different levels or kinds of organization. The gene complex, as it exists in a zygote, is only a portion in space and time of a particular stage of organization, and the inherited coils of DNA operate within a cellular environment and, indeed, interact with this environment. A multitude of environmental effects, intracellular and extracellular, internal and external, influence the way in which the genes operate, and the genes, in turn, influence their immediate biochemical environment. These interacting systems also operate in time, and future developmental events are affected by past gene-environment interactions. Even the genes themselves constitute an active environment for other genes. The complexities of a developing living system are immense, and this much is becoming clear: Heredity and environment are an inseparably fused system.

Although this modern epigenetic principle is generally applied to the development of structure and function, it is equally applicable to behavior. Perhaps it is even more essential to the study of behavior, because the overt actions of an organism represent the functioning of the organism as a whole on its highest level of organization.

The bases for some characteristics are laid down early in development. The biochemical precursors for the determination of blood type, for example, are probably irreversibly organized at some very early embryonic stage. Subsequent environmental changes cannot do much toward altering blood type, although future techniques in immunology and whole blood transfusions may show that some specialized kinds of environmental control can change blood types. Medical prognosticators are even now talking about the possibilities of controlling heredity. This is, in effect, controlling the genetic code by means of environmental manipulation.

At the other extreme one might put women's fashions. This characteristic, developed significantly later in life than blood type, is strongly influenced by cultural factors that may be transitory and changeable. Hemlines may go up or down with the whims of fashion, but even here the genetic and early developmental factors play some role. Replace one X-chromosome with a Y-chromosome, and it becomes highly improbable that the individual will be concerned with hemlines in the same way.

In formulating a scientific problem, it is important to ask logically valid questions, i.e., questions that do not contain a hidden assumption or unsubstantiated premise. In the analysis of behavior, the proper questions might be: How does this behavior develop? What are the factors that channel its development? How do these factors operate and within what limits? What are the adaptive properties of this behavior to the individual and to the species? These questions represent the second stage of behavioral study, that beyond the basic descriptive one. But even in the process of description, one must keep these analytical questions in mind so that the description itself will not be colored by a priori assumptions about the developmental mechanisms involved. As in all scientific observations, it is important, indeed, it is essential, to keep observations and interpretations clearly separate in one's thinking and writing.

### WHY STUDY ANIMAL BEHAVIOR?

The study of animal behavior presents some rather potent arguments for its importance. Whether one studies the properties of the DNA code, the permeability of cell membranes, the function of the liver, or the electroencephalographic patterns of the human brain, the basic problem is always concerned with the functioning of the entire organism and how all these bits and pieces operate together. An expression of the total function of any organism is, of course, its behavior. In other words, what an animal does is the culmination of the interaction of all its existing parts and the interdependent development of all these parts.

The main unifying principle in biology is evolution, which is presently conceived as the process of natural selection operating on populations of organisms with variable hereditary constitutions. Although natural selection involves species formation and survival, at its root it depends upon the behavior of individual organisms that select mates and environmental niches. Thus, behavior becomes an important area of study to a biologist who is concerned to any degree with the evolutionary process.

Of direct practical value, the study of animal behavior is closely related to the study of human behavior. The use of experimental animals permits us to gain data applicable to human behavior that cannot be obtained from human studies alone.

Animal behavior has, in recent years, occupied the interests of biologists in virtually all areas of research, including ecology, genetics, physiology, endocrinology, and even molecular biology. It is in this sense that we can view animal behavior as the nexus of all biological fields.

## Suggested Readings

Beach, F. A. 1950. The Snark was a Boojum. *Amer. Psychologist,* 5: 115–124.
Darwin, C. 1872. *The Expression of the Emotions in Man and Animals.*
    Reprinted edition, 1965. University of Chicago Press: Chicago.
Novikoff, A. 1945. The concept of integrative levels and biology. *Science,*
    101: 209–215.

Pavlov, I. P. 1927. *Conditioned Reflexes.* (G. V. Anrep. trans. and ed.)
    Reprinted edition, 1960. Dover Publications: New York.
Schneirla, T. C. 1953. The concept of levels in the study of social phenomena.
    *In* Sherif, M., and C. W. Sherif (eds.), *Groups in Harmony and Tension.*
    Harper and Row, Publishers: New York. Pp. 54–75.
Schneirla, T. C. 1957. The concept of development in comparative psychology.
    *In* D. B. Harris (ed.), *The Concept of Development.* University of
    Minnesota Press: Minneapolis, Minn. Pp. 78–108.
Tinbergen, N. 1951. *The Study of Instinct.* Clarendon Press: Oxford.

# 3 METHODOLOGY

More than 60 years ago, C. Lloyd Morgan proposed a principle often referred to as *Morgan's Canon* (quoted earlier). He stated, in effect, that in the interpretation and explanation of any behavior of an animal, higher level psychological factors should not be invoked if lower, simpler conceptual levels provide an adequate explanation. In an obvious case, one can readily analyze the movements of a *Paramecium* toward food on the basis of chemical stimuli and cytoplasmic responses, and the assumption of any reasoning powers by the protozoan is unnecessary. In a less obvious example, the maternal behavior of a cat toward its kittens can be explained adequately by a study of sensory and hormonal factors, and a complex of interacting internal physiological and external situations existing between the parent and the young. The human concept of mother love is quite superfluous here.

Morgan's Canon is really an extension of an older philosophical statement by a fourteenth century Franciscan, William of Occam, who proposed that given an alternative between two hypotheses, the one accompanied by the fewer assumptions is to be preferred. This law of logic has come to be known as *Occam's razor* or the *Law of Parsimony,* on

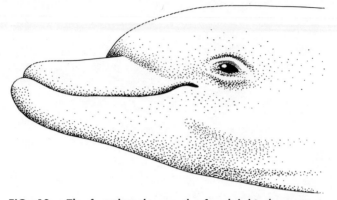

FIG. 13. The fact that the mouth of a dolphin happens to look like a human smile has given many people the impression that the dolphin is a happy, cheerful animal, whereas it is only docile and trainable. We actually know nothing about what happiness is to a dolphin.

which basis scientists always seek simpler explanations and avoid unnecessary assumptions and hypotheses.

Of all the biological sciences, behavior is the one in which these scientific principles are most often overlooked. It is very easy to interpret the behavior of an organism, particularly the "pleasant, friendly" behavior of a dog, cat, or porpoise, as if it has a human mind and human emotions. This type of erroneous thinking is called *anthropomorphism,* which is the assumption of the existence of a human mind inside the body of a non-human animal. Since neither a dog nor a flatworm can accurately communicate in words we can understand, we cannot assume that they think the same way we do. It is very likely that the behavior of animals other than man depends upon very different psychological processes because their anatomy and development are different from ours. (See Fig. 13.)

Newspapermen and pet-lovers are particularly prone to make such anthropomorphic interpretations. An example of this was a newspaper report some years ago about the annual flight of wild geese from a lake. A heart-rending tale was told of how two members of this flock returned to help one of their fellows who was so ill he could not fly. Reduced to essential facts, the story was that (a) the flock took off, but one remained behind; (b) two members of the flock returned and alighted next to the laggard; (c) a few minutes later all three took flight. As Thorndike once pointed out:

> Dogs get lost hundreds of times and no one ever notices it or sends an account of it to a scientific magazine. But let one find his

way from Brooklyn to Yonkers and the fact immediately becomes a circulating anecdote. Thousands of cats on thousands of occasions sit helplessly yowling and no one takes thought or writes to his friend the professor; but let one cat claw at the knob of a door supposedly as a signal to get out, and straightway this cat becomes the representative of the cat-mind in all the books.

## OBSERVATIONS

If we consider all the pitfalls, what rules and methods can we apply to avoid anthropomorphism and similar confusions among levels of organization? As in all things, advice is easier to give then to follow. How can one maintain complete objectivity in the face of a culturally developed tendency to be subjective?

One technique, which is applicable to all sciences, is to separate interpretations from factual observations. When taking the temperature of a liquid in a vessel or reading a number from a Geiger counter, it is easier to be objective, but even here machines are often constructed to record these readings on punch cards, and observers will repeat their observations and cross-check each other in order to protect against making errors in the direction the experimenter hopes his data will go.

Let us take a specific problem and see how one experimenter solved it. Some years ago, L. R. Aronson wanted to study the spawning behavior of a fish in which the male carries the eggs about in his mouth until they hatch. This species, one of the African mouth breeders (*Tilapia*), goes through a rather complex series of activities: The male and female form a pair and excavate a shallow depression in the sand; the female lays her eggs; the male fertilizes them and then scoops them up in his mouth. Before Dr. Aronson could begin to analyze this behavior in terms of the mechanisms that stimulate these activities, he had to describe the entire behavior pattern. He was not satisfied to sit and watch the fish go through their repertoire, and end up by reporting that "usually" the male did this, while "most of the time" the female did that. He recognized that, as in all biological observations, there is a degree of variability, and he wanted to give as objective a description as possible. He therefore divided the entire behavioral pattern into simple, short, easily described movements and recorded the frequency of occurrence of each and the relation of the occurrence of each movement to the occurrence of all the others. He also recoded the sequences of the movements and the duration of each. After repeating these observations many times with many different pairs of fish, he found he had amassed a large volume of numerical data. The data were analyzed by statistical methods and Dr. Aronson was then able to describe the behavior pattern in detail. More significantly, he was able to show just how variable the pattern was. (See Figs. 14 and 15.)

In another example, D. S. Blough wanted to determine the exact visual threshold in pigeons, i.e., the minimum amount of light that they could see. He placed his animals in a test chamber where they were taught to peck at a key in order to obtain a reward of a grain of corn. By using a combination of keys coupled with a spot of light that could be dimmed or brightened, the bird learned to peck at the right combination of keys to obtain the maximum reward when the light was just barely visible. The entire apparatus was operated automatically. In effect the bird was forced to make a choice and signal unequivocally: "yes," or "no." A "maybe" answer was not tolerated, and the automation of the apparatus prevented any subjective errors of observation on the part of the experimenter. By this technique, Dr. Blough was able to determine accurately what the bird's visual capacities were, and what factors could influence these capacities. (See Fig. 16.)

The details of Blough's technique are somewhat involved, but they are worthy of study from the point of view of methodology. Pigeons are readily trained to peck at an object or a panel on a wall when rewarded for these pecks by a grain of food. This reward, more properly known as a *reinforcement,* increases the probability of the appropriate peck, and a pigeon will continue to peck at the same target hundreds of times in succession under these conditions. Each bird was placed in a lightproof, soundproof box equipped with a lighted, translucent panel and two targets. The two targets, when touched by a pecking movement, would operate microswitches. First the bird was trained to peck at target A in the presence of light on the panel. Repeated pecks on A caused the light to dim and eventually go out completely. At this time, a food hopper would move into the box just long enough for the bird to obtain one or two seeds. Second, the bird was trained to peck on target B when the light went out, and this target activated the food hopper. Repeated pecks on target B, however, turned on or increased the light intensity on the panel. Eventually, the bird was trained to peck on A until the light was no longer visible, then shift to B to activate the food hopper. Appropriate electronic circuitry controlled the sequence of light intensity changes to insure that the bird would get the maximum reward at the point where the light intensity was nearest to the bird's threshold of vision. With minor modifications, this type of equipment can be used to study various aspects of sensory function in animals and has also been used to investigate learning and other phenomena.

Aronson's *Tilapia* and Blough's pigeons illustrate an important aspect of modern study of animal behavior. The observer need not rely on

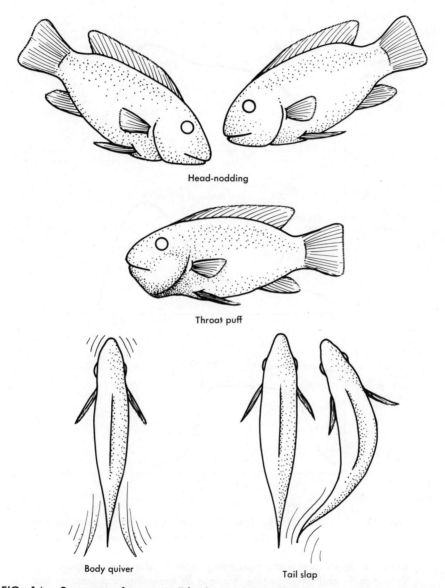

Head-nodding

Throat puff

Body quiver                    Tail slap

FIG. 14.   Sequence of events in *Tilapia spawning.* The sequence is not clear, but the several activities reflect different degrees of arousal and physiological preparation for spawning. In addition to the actions shown, more intense prespawning behavior includes nipping, nest-building (formation of a depression in the sand), nest passing, and spawning quivers.

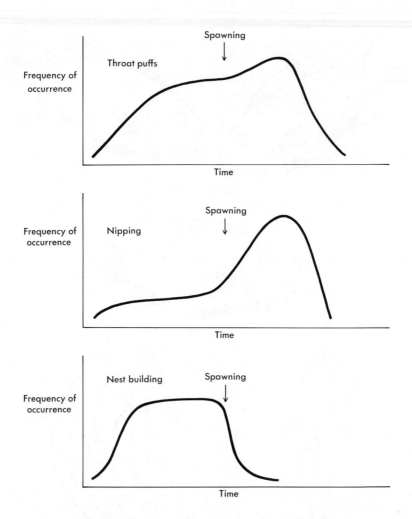

FIG. 15.   Graphs (derived from Aronson's data) show some of the results of a quantitative study of prespawning behavior in *Tilapia*. Each graph shows the frequency of certain activities over a period of about 4 hours preceding spawning and 2 hours after spawning. Throat-puffs and other actions increase as spawning approaches, and actually continue to increase after spawning for a short period of time. Nipping, however, increases slowly up to spawning, then peaks rapidly. Nest building reaches a maximum two or three hours prior to spawning and then drops off quickly. Each behavior pattern in the complex has its own antecedents and represents different levels of arousal.

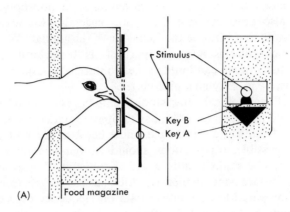

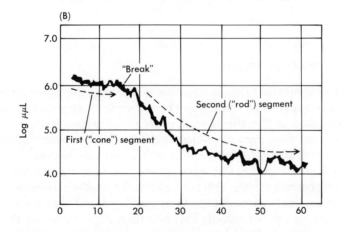

FIG. 16. (A) Schematic diagram of test chamber used to study visual thresholds in the pigeon. (B) Graph shows data on vision in the pigeon obtained by Blough. The brightness threshold of the pigeon changes with increased time in the dark. The graph shows a "break" that represents the threshold of the cone elements of the retina. Increased time in the dark increases the sensitivity (decreases the threshold) of the rod elements. The obtained curve is similar in many respects to that for humans. (After Donald S. Blough, "Dark Adaptation in the Pigeon," *J. Comp. Physiol. Psychol.,* vol. 49, 1956.)

approximations and ambiguous word descriptions, but can obtain accurate, objective data and reduce the human tendency to anthropomorphize. These examples also illustrate that there are basically two ways in which we can investigate and observe the behavior of an animal: We may either use some response that is normally part of its behavioral repertoire, (e.g., Aronson's fish) or we can build in, i.e. condition, a response to some specific stimulus, (e.g., Blough's pigeons).

Not all animal behavior studies can be controlled so conveniently, however, and the observer often has to operate under uncomfortable conditions in the field. Certain principles must be observed under all conditions. Whenever possible, observations should be handled numerically, so that variability can be studied with the aid of statistics, if necessary. The importance of measurement cannot be stressed too much, and the observer should be prepared to accumulate data on frequency of occurrence, intensity, duration, and sequential patterning. At the beginning of a study it is often not clear what to record as data and what to discard as irrelevant. Many times, seemingly irrelevant activities take on an unexpected importance, and if not recorded, these data may be irretrievably lost.

### EXPERIMENTAL STUDIES

Experimental work in behavior is not basically different from that in any other experimental science. The principle of control is essential. If one is interested in the effects of destruction of certain parts of the brain upon behavior, then control animals must be used in which sham operations are performed or other regions of the nervous system damaged. In other words, the experimenter must insure that only the manipulated factors are responsible for the observed effects. In another sense of the word, control means that the environment is regulated and that the number of extraneous variables is reduced. This is usually done by taking the animals into a laboratory. In the laboratory, as opposed to the field, observations can be made at the observer's convenience, and he can focus on what he is interested in and be prepared to record it. This second aspect of control is particularly important in behavioral study. In some instances, portions of the animal's natural environment can be fenced, and this, at least in part, reduces the vagaries of outdoor conditions and introduces some environmental control.

In behavioral experiments, many restrictions are placed upon the conditions of uniformity of the animals. Preferably, the subjects should be of the same genetic strain, but, further, their experience in development should be as uniform as possible. It is conceivable, for example, that there would be a behavioral difference between animals from a large litter and those from a small one. Seemingly inconsequential or irrelevant differences during development can often produce effects that might be attributed incorrectly to the effects of the experiment. Admittedly, it is often difficult, sometimes impossible, to maintain a desirable level of uniformity, and the experimenter often will try to eliminate these variables by random selection of his subjects.

It is rare indeed to obtain experimental results in which the data present clear and unequivocal conclusions, and it is virtually impossible to have a set of biological data where some variability does not exist. Reduction of the data to numerical values is usually desirable, because one can more easily treat the numbers with statistical methods, which need not be very complex. Sometimes an average, e.g., arithmetic mean, is sufficient, but generally the mean should be accompanied by some measure of variability. (See Fig. 17.) At times more complicated and elaborate statistical tests must be applied to the data. Although the theoretical bases for many of these methods may be highly involved and require specialized knowledge, most books on statistics written for biologists or psychologists give relatively easy formulas and directions. However, like any other technique, statistics must be used properly. Statistics will not demonstrate anything not already present in the data, and the use of statistics does not make the data any more reliable. It is, however, useful to employ statistical analysis to summarize and analyze your data and to demonstrate variability, differences, and similarities.

### TECHNIQUES

The basic tools for recording data are, of course, pencil and paper, but often things happen too fast, are too complex, or last too long a time. The observer must then rely on machinery to assist him in recording data. Photography, especially motion pictures, is a reliable tool, and the data can later be extracted from the film, frame by frame if need be. For certain types of observations, the tape recorder is extremely useful, because it will record data as fast as one can talk.

One widely used technique involves a pen and ink recorder equipped with many individual pens (Fig. 18). The record is made on a long roll of paper. The movement of each pen is controlled by a microswitch activated by touch. A bank of twenty such switches is set up, and the observer records each event on the rolling paper by a sort of touch typing system. Up to twenty different activities can be recorded. With this technique the duration of each activity can be determined and the interrelationships among the various activities can be accurately measured.

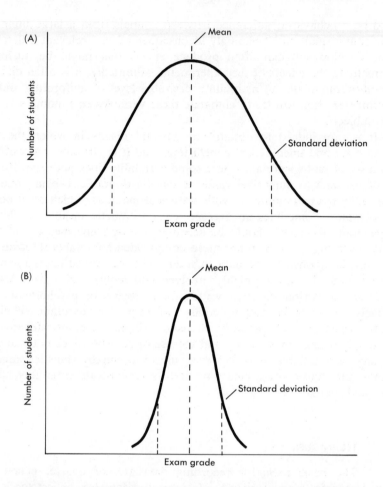

FIG. 17. The typical probability curve is the "bell-curve." Given a random group of students taking an examination, the average (mean) grade is the sum of the grades divided by the number of students. The standard deviation is one common statistical measure of the distribution of the data. In (A) and (B) the means may be the same, but the distribution is different.

In some cases the activity of the animal can be recorded automatically. The modern equivalent of Thorndike's problem box, is the operant test chamber developed by B. F. Skinner. Here the animal is trained to press one or more levers or to peck at targets (Fig. 19). The reward is delivered automatically, and the responses of the subjects are recorded on paper by machine (Fig. 20). By various combinations of relays and other

FIG. 18. Recording apparatus involving the use of an event recorder and a keyboard of switches. (After T. C. Schneirla and J.S. Rosenblatt, "Behavioral Organization and Genesis of the Social Bond in Insects and Mammals," *Amer. J. Orthopsychiatry,* vol. 31, 1961.)

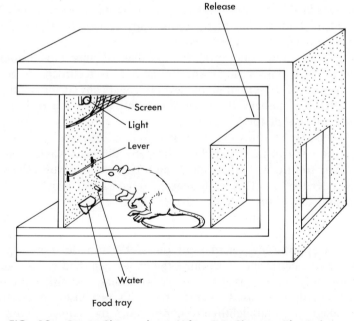

Release

Screen

Light

Lever

Water

Food tray

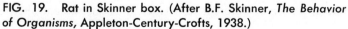

FIG. 19. Rat in Skinner box. (After B.F. Skinner, *The Behavior of Organisms,* Appleton-Century-Crofts, 1938.)

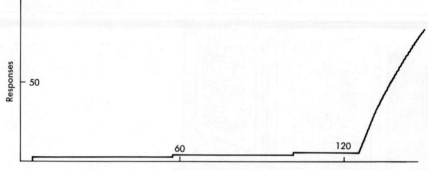

Time in minutes

FIG. 20.   Cumulative record of performance. Lever in Fig. 19 is connected to a recording apparatus. Because the recording paper is constantly moving at a known velocity, the observe can determine the rate at which the experimental animal is responding at any time. Response rates will change as a function of the rate at which food pellets are delivered (rate of reinforcement) and other experimental manipulations take place. After three widely spaced responses, the animal sharply increased its response rate. (After B.F. Skinner, *The Behavior of Organisms,* Appleton-Century-Crofts, 1938.)

electrical circuits, the subject can actually control its own reward schedule and variations in the stimulus. This type of apparatus is limited only by the ingenuity of the builder, and there are as many variations on this theme as there are experiments and experimenters.

One of the disadvantages of the so-called Skinner box, however, is that in most cases only a single specific activity is recorded. A good example involves the observation of several genetically distinct strains of mice in such test chambers. If one considers only the records of bar-presses and reinforcements of food pellets, the several strains appear remarkably similar. When the bar-pressing behavior itself is observed, however, it is clear that the bar can be manipulated in many different ways. Some mice use only their front paws; others climb on top of the bar; still others climb over and under the bar. These differences are consistent for the strains, yet the recording apparatus will not detect them.

In our own laboratory we developed a technique for the study of hearing in fishes. The fish was trained to swim across a shallow hurdle whenever an appropriate sound went on. If the fish did not respond, it received a mild electric shock. Because the experiment had to be conducted in a soundproof box, it was not possible to observe the fish directly, and photoelectric cells were used to track the fish's responses. A control apparatus, called the Audioichthyotron, presented the sound stimuli in an appropriate sequence of different intensities. This instrument also recorded the speed and kind of response, and whether the fish swam across the hurdle during a trial when the sound was on or in between trials. In this way, a number of behavioral activities were observed and recorded.

Extremely complex machinery has been devised for certain experiments. Some apparatus includes a system that feeds the data directly into a computer. This complexity is devised in order to collect *all* pertinent data in an objective fashion as rapidly and accurately as possible.

An important point to remember, with regard to data-gathering techniques, is that the observer can never gather *all* the data—except possibly with some future three-dimensional motion picture camera that will also record sounds and smells. Even if one could record all the events, only a small fraction would be pertinent to the experiment. The observer, therefore, has to select the kind of data he will collect, make some predictions as to what might be pertinent, and design his recording techniques accordingly. This may be as simple as deciding where to place a chair, or as complex as building a special electronic machine.

In general, it is wise to begin with the simplest methods and to develop more complex apparatus as needed. If this caution is not followed, one may purchase elaborate and expensive equipment which does not gather the desired data.

### SYNTHESIS

Data are not collected for their own sake, but in order to answer some specific question. As many students have discovered, the formulation of the right question is often one of the most difficult facets of research. In the study of animal behavior there are perhaps more pitfalls for the unwary than in any other branch of biological science. It is sometimes too easy to formulate a problem containing unwarranted assumptions, and this can affect the entire design of an experiment in such a way that the data become meaningless.

The first level of research in animal behavior is purely descriptive, that is, to enumerate in detail all the activities of the species that constitute a particular behavior pattern. From a theoretical point of view, this phase is probably the simplest, because one need not form a hypothesis or erect a theory. The observer must maintain objectivity and follow the rigid principle of not confusing observations with interpretations. Observations usually lead to new questions, some of which require a different approach for solution.

The second level of research is generally experimental, in which a search is made for mechanisms and explanations. Sometimes the mechanisms controlling a particular behavior can be deduced from observations alone, but usually this technique only results in the formulation of an hypothesis that must be tested by experimental means. In this formulation, the Law of Parsimony should be observed in order to design a specific experiment with the proper variables and controls to test the hypothesis.

Finally, some researchers actually use their tested hypotheses to formulate a comprehensive theory. As in all fields of science, a theory must be constantly tested and revised as new data are added.

## Suggested Readings

Aronson, L. R. 1949. An Analysis of Reproductive Behavior in the Mouth-breeding Cichlid Fish, *Tilapia macrocephala. Zoologica,* 34: 133–158.

Blough, D. S. 1961. Experiments in Animal Psychophysics. *Scientific American,* 205: 113–122.

Tavolga, W. N. 1964. Psychophysics and hearing in fish. *Natural History,* 73: 34–41.

Tobach, E., T. C. Schneirla, L. R. Aronson and R. Laupheimer. 1962. The ATSL: An observer-to-computer system for a multivariate approach to behavioral study. *Nature,* 194: 257–258.

Wecker, S. C. 1964. Habitat selection. *Scientific American,* 211: 109–116.

# 4  SENSORY CAPACITIES

The basic behavioral characteristic of cytoplasm, as mentioned earlier, is its *irritability*. All living materials respond, in some way, to environmental changes called *stimuli*. A stimulus, then, represents some change that is detectable by the organism. In the simplest situation, the entire organism receives and responds to the stimulus, as, for example, an *Amoeba* responds to a microneedle or foreign chemical.

The receptor equipment of many protozoans consists of temporary cytoplasmic organelles. Some of the more specialized forms possess light-sensitive spots, and cilia or flagella may be considered receptors of mechanical stimuli. For example, *Euglena,* a primitive type of green algae, possesses a light-sensitive structure (stigma) at its anterior end as shown in Fig. 21. By means of this stigma, the *Euglena,* can orient toward a light source. Such behavior is adaptive, because the organism depends primarily on photosynthesis for its nutrition. Most colonial protozoans and sponges fall into the category in which receptor specialization is at a low level.

The next level of sensory organization is represented by the coelenterates, in which some ectodermal cells develop enhanced sensitivities to chemical, mechanical, or light stimuli. Some jellyfish and other inverte-

43

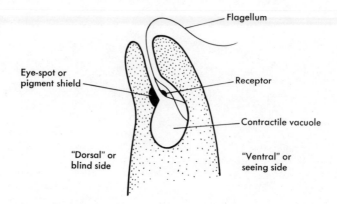

FIG. 21. Side view of *Euglena*. (After G.S. Fraenkel
and D.L. Gunn, *The Orientation of Animals*, Dover Publications, 1961.)

brates have spheroids of cells with hairs (statocysts) (Fig. 22) that are
sensitive to water displacements. The statocysts are probably sensitive to
changes in position and, possibly, to water currents, and represent the most
complex of the sensory mechanisms among coelenterates.

The higher multicellular animals have a sensory organization consisting of many integrated tissues and true organs. The complexity of organization varies greatly. For example, the eye of *Planaria* consists simply of
several light-sensitive nerve endings shaded on one side for directionality.
The eye of the annelid *Nereis* not only has more light-sensitive endings, but
also a primitive lens that can concentrate light on the retina. The compound
eye of an arthropod, the crayfish, has multiple elements so that the entire
structure becomes sensitive to the detection of movement and flicker (Fig.
23).

The differences between sense organs at the various levels of organization involve not only differences in complexity, but also differences in kind.
The vertebrate eye is not simply a more elaborate version of the flatworm
eye-spot. It shows profound differences in embryonic origin, in organization of the sensitive receiving cells, and even in the chemistry of the receptor mechanism.

Each individual unit of the compound eye of an insect covers a visual
field that overlaps those of its neighbors, and the compound eye appears to
be highly sensitive to the alternation of light and dark. This is termed
sensitivity to *flicker*. The vertebrate eye tends to fuse a series of images that
go on and off at a rate of 15 or more times per second into a continuous,
smoothly changing picture. The entire principle of motion pictures takes

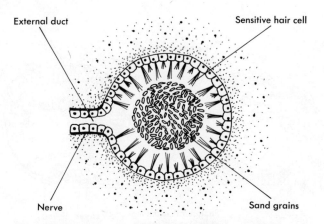

External duct

Sensitive hair cell

Nerve

Sand grains

FIG. 22. Section through the statocyst of *Pecten inflexus*. By orienting itself so that the granules stimulate the lower hairs, the animal can maintain its position with respect to gravity. This, therefore, is a simple equilibrium sense, and it can also receive low frequency vibrations. (After J. A. Colin Nicol, *The Biology of Marine Animals*, Sir Isaac Pitman and Sons Ltd, 1960.)

advantage of our insensitivity to flicker. The insect eye, however, is capable of resolving an image into individual flickers at a much higher rate, perhaps up to 100 or 150 pictures per second. In addition, most insects can detect light in the ultraviolet range, but discriminate poorly in the red portion of the spectrum.

It is well known that honeybees can distinguish between simple shapes and prefer certain flower shapes over others. At one time, it was believed that bees possessed some innate shape-recognizing mechanisms that evoked an appropriate response when the proper flower was present. Some experiments, with both trained and untrained bees, have shown this to be untrue. Bees have difficulty in distinguishing between simple shapes such as solid circles, squares, triangles, and oblongs, whereas more complex figures (more complex to us, that is) such as crosses, Y's, hollow angular shapes, and radiating and intersecting lines appear to give them less trouble. A pattern of small checkerboard squares, for example, is preferred over concentric circles or broad, radiating lines. On the basis of discrimination tests with conditioned bees and preference tests with untrained bees, it is clear that bees use some properties of shapes other than the over-all pattern (Fig. 24).

When a bee approaches a flower or one of the test figures, it hovers briefly and then alights. While hovering, the bee scans the figure with its

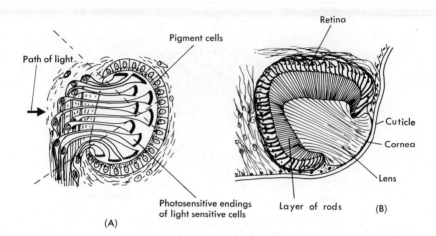

(A)

(B)

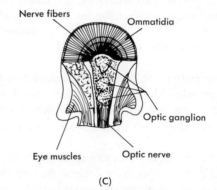

(C)

**FIG. 23.** Schematic comparison of eyes of (A) *Planaria,* (B) *Nereis,* and (C) crayfish.

multifaceted compound eyes, much as we scan a line of print, except that we move our eyes, and the bee moves its whole body. Each unit (ommatidium) of the bee's eye has only a very narrow visual angle, and the scanning produces a series of rapid flickers of dark and light on each ommatidium. A figure with a complex outline, many lines, or many separate pieces will have a stronger flickering effect than a smooth, simple perimeter.

In short, when an insect looks at a flower, it sees something very different from what we do and reacts to properties of the visual field that

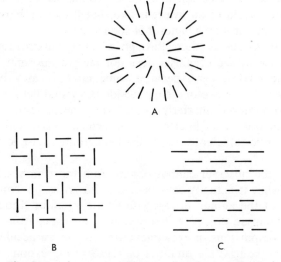

The bees show a preference for the small pieces arranged as in A rather than B or C. If A is removed, the bees then show no clear preference for either B or C.

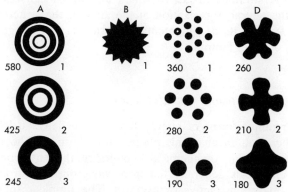

Other patterns used to test the effect of length of outline on a bee's recognition (the figures give an index of the length of outline). Bees trained to A-1 went equally to C-1, to A-2 equally to B-1 and C-2. But bees trained to C-1 or C-2 would not visit A-1 and one trained to D-2 ignored A-2.

FIG. 24.   Figures illustrating flicker effect. (After J. D. Carthy, *An Introduction to the Behaviour of Invertabrates,* George Allen & Unwin Ltd., 1962.)

we might not notice or be sensitive to. Of course we do not know exactly what the visual world of an insect is like, but it can probably be approximated by looking through a handful of soda straws.

Sense organs act as filters through which environmental changes are received. Obviously the organism does not receive information on all conditions of the environment, because some changes may be outside the sensitive range of its receptors, e.g., outside the visual field, beyond hearing range, etc. In addition, interfering signals may mask some of the environmental information. This interference is termed *noise,* and the energy of the *signal* must be sufficiently above the background noise level if it is to be detected.

Because the observer cannot obtain from the animal an accurate description of what it actually sees or hears, he bases his conclusions upon the behavior of the animal in response to the stimulus. Indeed, it is often difficult to obtain an objective description of an event from a human subject, as any comparisons of eyewitness accounts of an accident will reveal. Among human beings, the qualities of sensory impressions will vary with their education, sex, state of mind, and even their digestive state. The nature of a given sensory impression must be even more varied among organisms as different as flatworms, clams, insects, fishes, and birds. The qualities of the stimulus object to which an animal can respond are dependent on the neural organization of the animal, the structure of its central nervous system, its developmental experience, physiological condition, and a variety of other factors.

### CLASSES OF STIMULI AND RECEPTORS

Four major forms of energy that can be detected by living organisms are chemical, mechanical, photic, and thermal. The most basic is probably the detection of chemical changes in the environment. Among protozoans, chemicals generally fall into two groups according to the responses they evoke: attractive or aversive. The simple responses that can be observed are either an approach toward or a withdrawal from the stimulus source. In many cases, the same chemical can produce either an approach or withdrawal depending upon the concentration of the chemical, i.e., the intensity of the stimulation.

Specialized responses to specific chemicals often accompany the evolution of different organizations of cells forming sense organs and arise with the evolution of specific adaptations in sensory capacities and in behavior. Thus, in some species of moths, the two sexes are attracted to each other over distances of miles by concentrations of specific chemicals

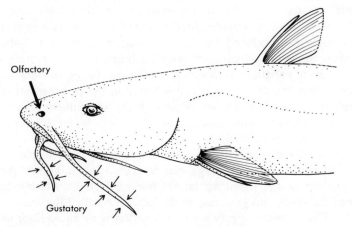

FIG. 25. Location of olfactory and gustatory organs in cat-
fish.

that are far below levels detectable by our instruments. Salmon are able to
find their home streams during their upstream migrations by recognizing
the chemicals specific to those areas.

Chemical sensitivity is mediated by two classes of receptors. Reception of minute concentrations of chemicals carried over long distances
through the air is usually called *olfaction,* i.e., the sense of smell. Reception of chemicals through a liquid medium, generally in association with
food, is called *gustation,* i.e., the sense of taste. In aquatic animals, this
separation is often not clear. In fishes, for example, both the nasal organs
and taste buds are sensitive to certain chemicals in the water. The distinction between the two senses is based upon the sensitivity to different chemicals and the location and structure of the receptor organs. Olfaction, a
highly sensitive sense in fishes, is a function of specialized cells lining the
inside of the nasal capsules and supplied by the olfactory nerve. Taste
buds, on the other hand, are less sensitive and may be found not only in the
mouth but on the lips, around the mouth, and even, in some species, on the
body and tail. (See Fig. 25.)

Another type of energy detection, probably as primitive as chemical
sensitivity, is the reception of mechanical stimuli (mechano-reception or
touch). The movement of its watery medium was probably one of the first
environmental changes to affect the primeval protozoa, and it is interesting
to follow the evolution of mechano-reception to the ends of the various
branches of the animal kingdom.

A specialization in mechano-reception is shown by the formation of
two types of sensitive hair cells with very different thresholds of excitation.

A highly sensitive type, found, for example, in the lateral line organ of fishes, is responsive to minute displacements (i.e., movements) of water such as might be produced by the swimming movements of other fishes, water currents, or low-frequency sound vibrations. This system of sense organs is even capable of detecting the presence of obstacles at some distance. A less-sensitive type of cell is found in the ectoderm of coelenterates and at the base of certain bristles in the integument of arthropods. This type responds to direct contact, and is, therefore, an organ of touch in the classic sense. (See Fig. 26.)

The step from sensitivity to water movements (i.e., displacement) to acoustic sensitivity (i.e., hearing) can be traced in the vertebrates. A cephalic portion of the primitive lateral line evolved by sinking under the skin, into the skull, and gave rise to the labyrinth called the inner ear. (See Fig. 27.) This structure probably first functioned as an equilibrium receptor, with the hair cells stimulated by movements of the fluids in its enclosed canals. Primitive fishes also evolved a sac that could be filled with air. This air bladder basically functioned to assist the buoyancy of the animal. A new function of the air bladder thus evolved. The animal could now receive pressure vibrations, since the air bladder was the only part not transparent to waterborne sounds. These vibrations were then transmitted to the inner ear. Some fishes even possess a series of small bones which lead from the air bladder to the inner ear (Fig. 28), and transmit sound in a manner analogous to that of the middle ear bones in mammals. Thus, the sense of hearing evolved from simple mechano-reception, and the terrestrial animals retained the enclosed labyrinth, which functions as both an equilibrium receptor and an acoustic receptor.

A third group of receptors is concerned with the detection of photic energy, i.e., light. Light is usually defined as the particular portion of the spectrum of electromagnetic radiation that is detectable by the human eye, although the ultraviolet and infrared portions of the spectrum are also included within this general definition. The structures that respond to stimulation within this range of wavelengths are termed organs of vision. Among animals, these light receptors vary not only in their sensitivity to light but also in their sensitivity to different portions of the spectrum.

Visual organs in animals can be divided into four groups on the basis of organizational level. The simplest of these is represented by light-sensitive *stigma* present in some protozoa. Such structures respond to major changes in total light energy, are poor in sensitivity, and are not capable of any discrimination of form. The eyespots of flatworms, annelid worms, and some mollusks and echinoderms are little better in sensitivity, but they do show a major advance in that they consist of an aggregation of specialized receptor cells located in the most convenient region for light

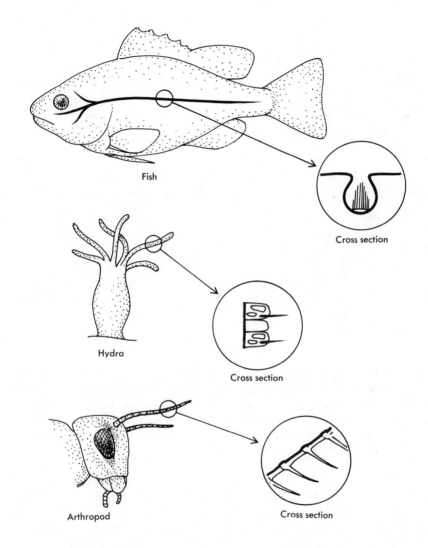

Fish

Cross section

Hydra

Cross section

Arthropod                    Cross section

FIG. 26.  Mechano-receptors in fish, *Hydra,* and arthropod.

reception. Some of these eyespots may possess a primitive lens that increases their sensitivity. They all transmit their received information in the
form of coded nerve impulses to the central nervous system.

The compound eyes of arthropods and the eyes of vertebrates are the
two most highly evolved types of visual structures. Among arthropods,
especially insects, each eye is actually composed of up to thousands of

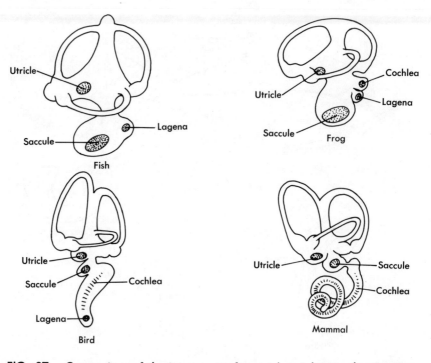

FIG. 27. Comparison of the inner ears of several vertebrates showing common features such as the semicircular canals. The acoustic portion of the inner ear, however, shows some profound differences. The presence of an elongate cochlea in birds and mammals gives them the ability to discriminate pitch to an extremely precise degree.      (After J. Z. Young, *Life of the Vertebrates*, Oxford University Press, 1962.)

units, called *ommatidia*. Each unit is complete in itself, with a lens and one or more sensitive cells. Such an eye cannot deliver to the central nervous system a photographic image of its field of vision, but it does provide a flickering field of light and dark spots and undoubtedly gives the animal a high degree of sensitivity for the perception of movement (Fig. 29).

The vertebrate eye is a more familiar structure and operates essentially like a camera with a lens that focusses light upon a light-sensitive surface (retina). (See Fig. 30.) Just as in a camera, the image has its limits of acuity, because the retina is composed of individual photosensitive cells—the rods and cones. The qualities that make the vertebrate eye unique are its high resolution for form and pattern, its effective light-gathering power, and its ability, in many species, to discriminate wave-

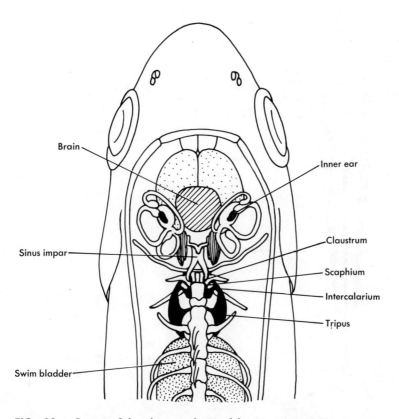

FIG. 28. Certain fishes have enhanced hearing sensitivity as a result of a chain of four pairs of small bones that couple the air bladder with the inner ear. (After J. Z. Young, *Life of the Vertebrates*, Oxford University Press, 1962.)

lengths, i.e., colors, to a degree not present in other visual organs. Among many vertebrates, the resolving power of the eye is enhanced by its ability to focus on near or distant objects either by changing the shape of the lens, by moving the lens, or by changing the position of the retina. It is interesting to note that one other group of animals developed eyes of this type. The cephalopods (e.g., squid, octopus, etc.) possess eyes that operate like vertebrate eyes, with a lens, retina, and iris, but in embryonic development the two types are quite different. The resemblance of the eyes of these specialized mollusks to vertebrate eyes represents a classic case of convergence of evolutionary development in unrelated groups.

A less well-known sense in animals is the one that detects changes in temperature. Some thermal sense organs are basically visual receptors that

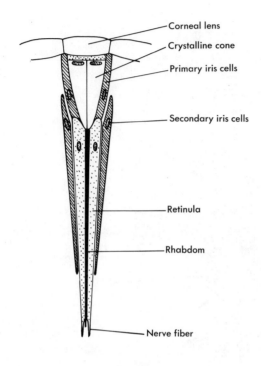

Corneal lens

Crystalline cone

Primary iris cells

Secondary iris cells

Retinula

Rhabdom

FIG. 29. Diagram of a generalized ommatidium of an insect
eye.

Nerve fiber

are specialized for infrared detection. Separate cold and heat receptors
have been demonstrated in many animals.

In recent years, a new sense organ has been discovered: an electro-
sensitive receptor in certain fishes. Some fishes, such as the electric eel and
a few other groups of species, are capable of emitting an electrical pulse
which surrounds the animal with an electrical field. If any nearby object or
other fish distorts this field, the emitter fish is capable of detecting such a
change by means of specialized groups of cells in its skin. (See Fig. 31.)
Some nonelectric fishes have been found to possess electro-sensitive organs
that may make them sensitive to electric fields produced by other organisms.

The detection of magnetic fields by animals has long been a subject of
research, but, thus far, most experiments have given negative results, and
the few positive ones have been looked on with skepticism. Similarly, there
is no evidence to indicate that any animal possesses any special detector for
radioactivity, although X rays, radium emissions, or other ionizing radia-
tions certainly affect the organism.

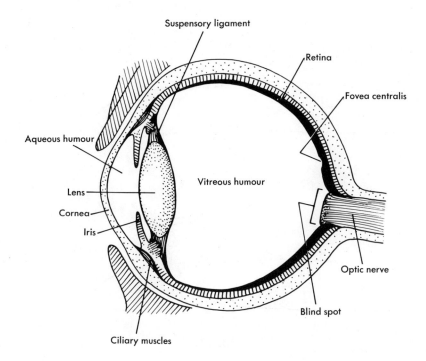

FIG. 30.    Detail of vertebrate eye.

## METHODS OF STUDY

Fundamentally, the function of the sense organs can be investigated by only two methods: neurophysiological and behavioral. The neurophysiological approach utilizes the fact that information received by a
sense organ is transformed into an energy change conducted along nerve
fibers. This has been likened to the transmission of voice signals along
telephone wires, but this analogy cannot be carried far. A nerve fiber can
only indicate the presence or absence of a signal, in accordance with the
*all-or-none law.* After the neurophysiologist successfully inserts his electrodes into a nerve fiber, he can only detect a series of electrical on-and-off
signals (spikes). The reactions of the sense organ to the different qualities
of the stimulus can only be transformed into a simple code in which the
main variable is the repetition rate of the spikes. (See Fig. 32.) In some
sense organs, this rate is directly proportional to the frequency of the stimulations, but in many types the rate of spike production is related in a more
complex way to the intensity of the stimulus.

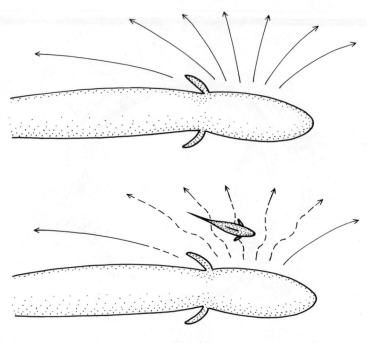

FIG. 31.

By means of this "wire-tapping," the neurophysiologist can discover many important properties of the sense organ. In some cases he can detect the electrical changes that take place in the sensory cells themselves, before the coding in the nerve fibers has taken place. The detection of these receptor potentials can give additional information about the reactivity of the sense organs. These techniques can not only tell us how sensitive the organ is and what qualitative and quantitative changes in the stimulus it can detect, but also enable us to investigate the physical and chemical bases of the detection process.

For the study of behavior, however, the next step in the sensory process is more important, i.e., what does the animal do with the stimuli it receives? The coded spike potentials conducted along the nerve from the sense organ to the central nervous system mix with similarly coded information from other sensory and integrative areas of the nervous system, and, finally, the animal responds by doing something the observer can detect and record. This response is generally adaptive and is related to past responses of the organism and its genetic and developmental background.

The distinction between these two levels of investigation can be exemplified by the problem of whether or not cats have color vision.

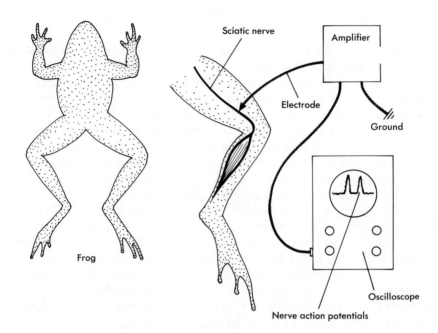

FIG. 32. An impulse travelling along a nerve consists of a wave of ionic changes on the surface of the nerve fiber. These changes can be detected by an appropriate electrode and an amplifier and then be visually displayed on the screen of an oscilloscope.

The structure of the retina and a study of the electrical activity of the optic nerve shows that the eye can detect differences in wavelengths of light and does transmit this information, in code, to the central nervous system. Most behavioral studies, however, have demonstrated that cats cannot discriminate among different colors providing that all other qualities of light intensity and purity are equal. The animal, therefore, does not necessarily use all the information it receives. Some recent work, however, has shown that, after prolonged and intensive training, cats will discriminate colors when prevented from using brightness cues. As the context of the situation varies, so does the response. The response of a hungry cat to the sight of a mouse is clearly different from the response of a well-fed cat. Apparently the central nervous system "ignores" nonpertinent information, although it is quite possible that the information is stored for future reference, i.e., as *memory*. Unfortunately, the observer can only deal with the overt response of the animal, although in recent years advances in electrophysiology have made it possible to detect correlated activities in the brain.

### PSYCHOPHYSICS

In the 1860's Gustav Fechner established a branch of psychology called *psychophysics*. This study of the quantitative aspects of sensory function attempts to measure the sensory capacities of an organism by considering its responses to controlled stimuli. This type of investigation was once confined to the human species, but it has now been broadened to include many other animals. Two important principles are basic to psychophysics: *threshold,* and the existence of a nonlinear relationship between *stimulus intensity* and *sensation level.* Stimulus intensity is the measure of the energy impinging upon the sense organ, and sensation level is the subject's own judgment of the strength of this stimulus.

Loosely defined, a *threshold* is the lowest intensity level of a stimulus that can be detected by a sense organ. However, psychophysics deals primarily with the response of the individual and becomes concerned with the response threshold, rather than the sensory threshold. In behavioral studies, reference is commonly made to the response threshold. A more precise definition of a threshold must take into account the fact that it is a statistical rather than an absolute value. Given any low intensity stimulus, there is some measurable probability that the organism will respond. As the stimulus intensity is lowered, the probability of response decreases to zero; as the intensity is raised, the probability of response approaches 100%. The threshold can be set arbitrarily at any point in this probability scale, but the 50% point is the one most frequently chosen by modern psychophysicists. For practical purposes, threshold can be defined as the stimulus intensity level at which there is a 50-50 chance that the organism will give a positive response. (See Fig. 33.)

Methods of determining thresholds are many and varied, but, in general, the most efficient utilize some conditioned response on the part of the subject, e.g., bar-pressing, avoidance of a shock, change in heart rate, etc. Numerous statistical methods have been developed which determine thresholds with a considerable degree of accuracy. With these methods, the animal is exposed to stimuli at various intensities in some predetermined pattern so that the observer's bias is virtually eliminated.

A second principle in psychophysics is known as the *Weber-Fechner law.* As defined by Fechner, the law states that a logarithmic relationship exists between the actual stimulus intensity and the intensity as it appears to the subject. This is given by the formula $I = C \log S,$ where $I$ is the sensation level, $S$ is the stimulus intensity, and $C$ is some constant. In acoustics, this law was the basis for the measurement of sound level in *decibels.* Sound is usually measured in terms of pressure (i.e., force per unit area), because a sound wave consists of alternate compressions and

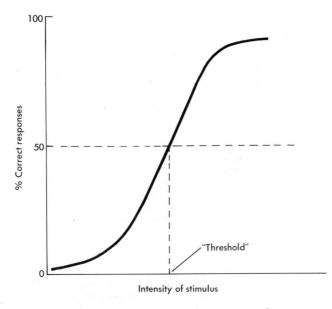

FIG. 33.   Psychometric function graph.

rarefactions of the medium. The decibel is defined as 20 log $p_1/p_o$, in which $p_o$ is a reference level and $p_1$ is the stimulus pressure. Thus, sound pressure is always a measurement relative to some standard, and the decibel scale is logarithmic. Similar equations are commonly used to express relative intensities of light and even electricity. In acoustics, the reference level commonly used is 0.0002 dyne/cm², because this happens to be the threshold of human hearing at a frequency of 1000 cycles per second, although one can set the reference level at any point that is convenient. There are two major advantages to using decibels to express stimulus intensities: First, it is easier to deal with logarithms because they can be added and subtracted and the awkwardness of operating with decimal fractions is reduced; second, the logarithmic law conforms approximately to the way in which sense organs operate. (See Fig. 34.)

How close the Weber-Fechner Law conforms to actual sensory systems is a matter of some debate. There is no question that the relation of stimulus intensity and sensation level is not a simple linear equation, but recent investigations have shown that the logarithmic law is an oversimplification. Apparently, sense organs conform to some other type of equation, and different sensory systems in different animals do not conform to the same equations. Nevertheless, the Weber-Fechner Law is still used as a practical, convenient means of expressing and measuring sensation level.

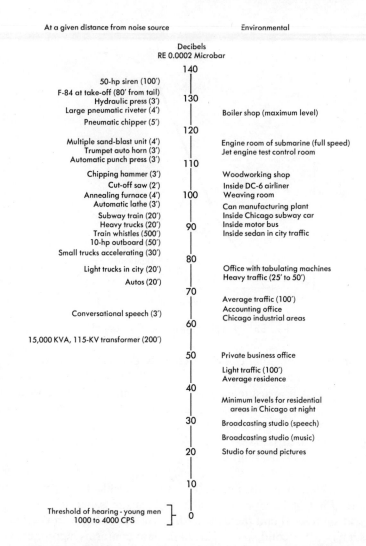

| At a given distance from noise source | Decibels RE 0.0002 Microbar | Environmental |
|---|:---:|---|
| | 140 | |
| 50-hp siren (100') | | |
| F-84 at take-off (80' from tail) | | |
| Hydraulic press (3') | 130 | |
| Large pneumatic riveter (4') | | Boiler shop (maximum level) |
| Pneumatic chipper (5') | | |
| | 120 | |
| Multiple sand-blast unit (4') | | Engine room of submarine (full speed) |
| Trumpet auto horn (3') | | Jet engine test control room |
| Automatic punch press (3') | 110 | |
| Chipping hammer (3') | | Woodworking shop |
| Cut-off saw (2') | | Inside DC-6 airliner |
| Annealing furnace (4') | 100 | Weaving room |
| Automatic lathe (3') | | Can manufacturing plant |
| Subway train (20') | | Inside Chicago subway car |
| Heavy trucks (20') | 90 | Inside motor bus |
| Train whistles (500') | | Inside sedan in city traffic |
| 10-hp outboard (50') | | |
| Small trucks accelerating (30') | 80 | |
| Light trucks in city (20') | | Office with tabulating machines |
| Autos (20') | | Heavy traffic (25' to 50') |
| | 70 | |
| | | Average traffic (100') |
| | | Accounting office |
| Conversational speech (3') | | Chicago industrial areas |
| | 60 | |
| 15,000 KVA, 115-KV transformer (200') | | |
| | 50 | Private business office |
| | | Light traffic (100') |
| | | Average residence |
| | 40 | |
| | | Minimum levels for residential areas in Chicago at night |
| | 30 | Broadcasting studio (speech) |
| | | Broadcasting studio (music) |
| | 20 | Studio for sound pictures |
| | 10 | |
| Threshold of hearing - young men 1000 to 4000 CPS | 0 | |

FIG. 34. Typical over-all sound levels. (From A.P.G. Peterson and E. E. Gross, Jr., *Handbook of Noise Measurement,* General Radio Co., 1963.)

In recent years, there has been some doubt about the validity of the threshold concept. Some investigators have pointed to the fact that psychophysics deals with *response thresholds,* and that the context of the testing situation can alter the results. If, for example, one animal is punished severely for errors (by electric shock, or other noxious stimulus), and another is punished mildly or not at all, the former may give a significantly lower threshold than the latter. The investigator, therefore, is dealing with threshold values that are not absolutes, but are valid only for his particular experimental situation. Furthermore, the statistical aspects of threshold determination indicate that here is no absolute threshold as such, but that a threshold represents a stimulus level at which there is a probability of both positive and negative responses.

## Suggested Readings

van Bergeijk, W. A. 1967. The evolution of vertebrate hearing. *In Contributions to Sensory Physiology,* Vol. 2. (W. D. Neff, ed.) Academic Press Inc.: New York. Pp. 1–49.

Carthy, J. D. 1958. *An Introduction to the Behavior of Invertebrates.* Hafner Publishing Co.: New York.

Green, D. M., and J. A. Swets 1966. *Signal Detection Theory and Psychophysics.* John Wiley & Sons: New York.

Hodgson, E. S. 1961. Taste receptors. *Scientific American,* 204: 135–144.

Lissman, H. W. 1963. Electric location by fishes. *Scientific American,* 208: 50–59.

Stevens, S. S. 1961. The psychophysics of sensory function. *In Sensory Communication.* (W. A. Rosenblith, ed.) John Wiley & Sons: New York. Pp. 1–33.

Tansley, K. 1950. Vision. *In* Physiological Mechanisms in Animal Behaviour. *Symp. Soc. Exp. Biol.,* No. 4: 19–33.

Wilson, E. O. 1963. Pheromones. *Scientific American,* 208: 100–114.

# 5   INTEGRATION

One of the most striking aspects of animal behavior is the fact that the entire organism operates in a coordinated fashion. In the course of locomotion, a commonplace activity, many muscles work so smoothly together that the act of taking a step or sweeping the tail in swimming appears to be a single continuous movement of the whole animal. All this locomotor activity is constantly guided by the sense organs, whose received environmental information is instantaneously sifted, reorganized, and interpreted in the light of the internal physiological states and current external requirements. The entire developmental history of the organism, from its days as an ovum, is incorporated in the organism as we observe it at any moment. *Integration,* then, includes more than just the coordinated operations of an organism at a given point in time. Integration is the union of all parts of a dynamic, cytoplasmic system into an adaptively functioning organism.

As in other aspects of biology, there are levels of organization among the integrative systems, and the study of these levels of integration is, to a large extent, a study of the evolution and phylogeny of nervous systems.

FIG. 35. Myonemes (dark lines) of a ciliate. A system of interlacing fibrils near the surface of many protozoa function as both a conductile and contractile system. (After E. A. Minchin, *An Introduction to the Study of the Protozoa*, Edward Arnold, 1922.)

### UNICELLULAR INTEGRATION

Among protozoans, the single cell is the entire organism, and its small size enables it to operate as a unit with the minimum of specialization of parts for integration. A stimulus received at one point of the cell membrane is rapidly transmitted by chemical diffusion to all other parts of the organism. The entire organism is at once a receptor, conductor, effector, and integrator.

Even at this level, however, portions of the cell, e.g., light-sensitive stigma, are specialized. The ciliates are perhaps the most highly evolved of the protozoans, and the coordinated, wave-like action of cilia on the surface of a *Paramecium* is indicative of some integrative mechanism more complex than mere diffusion. A meshwork of fine threads can be demonstrated interconnecting the bases of the cilia, and these threads are thought to function as conductile pathways so that the activity of one cilium is transmitted to others (Fig. 35). The velocity of this transmission must determine the speed and pattern of ciliary movement, and the distribution of the cilia and the shape of the organism determine the pattern of locomotion. Thus, in many species, integration within a single cell can be quite complex, yet the behavioral repertoire and its capacities for variation and adjustment are strictly limited.

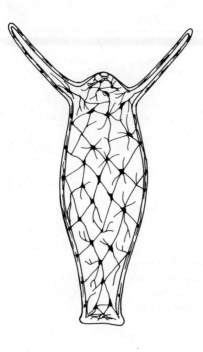

FIG. 36.   Nerve net of *Hydra*.

## DIFFUSE NERVOUS SYSTEMS

Among the most primitive of the metazoa, specializations among the component cells can be classified into three basic types by their function: receptor, transmitter, and effector. In the coelenterates, the ectodermal cell layer contains and gives rise to all three types. The sensory cells are sensitive to chemical changes and mechanical stimuli, and their excitation is transmitted to a network of nerve cells (neurons). The neurons conduct this excitation in the form of an electrochemical impulse along their cytoplasmic extensions (nerve fibers). The impulse is further transmitted to other neurons and to epitheliomuscular cells. The latter respond to this stimulus by contraction.

In these radially symmetrical animals, the level of integration is diffuse, and the responses of the organism to localized stimuli are also localized. Thus, the slight stimulation of a single tentacle in *Hydra* results in the response of that one tentacle or portion of the tentacle only (Fig. 36). The response spreads to the rest of the organism if the stimulus is intense or if the responding tentacle stimulates other portions of the animal during the course of its activity. There is no centralization of the nerve net, although some portions of the animal may have greater concentrations of receptor cells and neurons.

In the sponges, the level of integration is even simpler than in the coelenterates, and it is even questionable whether a sponge is to be considered a true metazoan or simply a colony of one-celled organisms. Each cell acts as a receptor and effector, and the contraction of one cell acts as a direct stimulus to its neighbors.

A more complex noncentral nervous system is illustrated by the Echinodermata (e.g., starfish, sea cucumbers, etc.). This phylum is an example of the high degree of specialization that can be achieved in a radially symmetrical animal. Instead of a diffuse network, the nerve fibers are organized into a number of main tracts consisting of a circumoral ring, five radial nerves, and numerous dermal plexi. The echinoderms also possess one other important advance in nervous systems: association neurons. These interconnect with other neurons, and the presence of this type of cell adds significantly to the integrative action of the nervous system. In spite of this, the behavioral repertoire of a starfish is quite limited, and its responses are localized to a considerable extent. Association neurons are also present in all the higher invertebrate and chordate groups.

Diffuse nervous systems are characteristic of sessile or slow-moving animals. Although some may be predators, these animals do not pursue their prey actively, but wait for the prey to blunder in or, like a starfish, move about slowly until some edible morsel is contacted. Sense organs in such animals are primarily short-range tactile types, and orientational abilities are extremely limited.

### STAGES OF CEPHALIZATION

The advent of bilateral symmetry among the metazoa was accompanied by profound changes in basic organization. One change, for example, was the development of a permanent, specialized head end, i.e., *cephalization*. A cephalized, bilaterally symmetrical animal has a ventral surface, which is basically a locomotor surface applied to the substrate, a dorsal surface, and, most important, an anterior end equipped with a battery of sense organs. Such an animal is oriented and usually mobile with regard to its environment.

With the concentration of sense receptors at the end most likely to encounter stimuli, there is a concomitant aggregation of nervous elements and a tendency toward nervous centralization. The primitive "brain" is essentially a sense-integrating mechanism, and its associative functions undoubtedly came later.

The flatworm, *Planaria*, is an example of a primitive cephalized animal. Its head possesses a pair of simple eyes and a concentration of

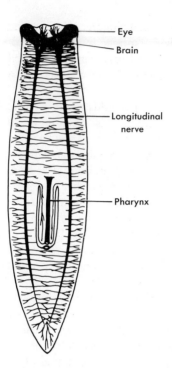

Eye

Brain

Longitudinal
nerve

Pharynx

FIG. 37.   Nervous system of Planaria.

chemical and mechanical sensory cells. Associated with these sense organs
are nerve fibers leading to a pair of cephalic ganglia, and leading from the
ganglia are nerve fibers to the muscles and others tissues of the rest of the
body. (See Fig. 37).

In the annelid worms, such as the earthworm (*Lumbricus*) and the
sand worm (*Nereis*), the basic segmental development and organization is
reflected in the structure of the nervous system. Each segment (metamere)
has some measure of autonomy, with a pair of excretory organs, a set of
muscles, and a pair of its own ganglia. All the sensory and motor nerve
fibers within a segment are integrated locally within the segmental ganglia,
but all the ganglia are interconnected so that the activity of any one segment is transmitted to other segments. In addition, the ventral nerve cord
possesses long "giant" fibers whose chief function seems to be to produce
over-all body contractions. The nervous control in these animals is divided
among the segments, but there is an overriding central control center in the
head. This, then, can be termed a "brain." (See Fig. 38.)

A ganglion is usually defined as an aggregation of nerve cell bodies,
and the neuronal connections that exist within a ganglion enable it to act as
an integrative center. In addition to the conduction of nerve impulses, gan-

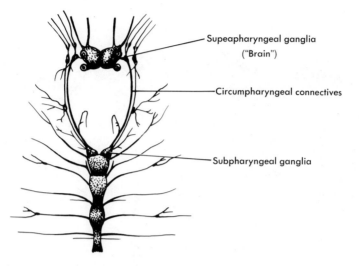

Supeapharyngeal ganglia
("Brain")

Circumpharyngeal connectives

Subpharyngeal ganglia

FIG. 38.   Nervous system of *Nereis.*

glion cells are often capable of secreting chemical materials different from the usual secretions of neurons. These secretions affect the physiology and behavior of the organism.

Among the many groups of invertebrates, nervous systems are quite varied in structure and degree of centralization, but the peak of evolutionary development of this type of ganglionated system appears to have been reached in the phylum Arthropoda. Although they still possess the basically segmental, ladderlike nervous organization, the most advanced forms among the insects show a significant amount of fusion and consolidation. (See Fig. 39.) The several ganglia that are combined to form the "brain" in the head are concerned chiefly with the highly developed sensory sys-. tems, whereas the thoracic "brain" is the main motor center.

The pinnacle of cephalization is achieved in the vertebrates, whose nervous system develops as a hollow dorsal tube, with segmentation appearing secondarily in the form of chains of nerves and ganglia. (See Fig. 40.)

The basic organization of the vertebrate nervous system is described adequately in any good zoology or comparative anatomy textbook and will not be covered here. However, we may note that basically cephalization is related to an organism's capacity to orient itself with respect to environment and specific stimuli. At each stage of increased cephalization and centralization, new behavioral properties appear, such as orientation

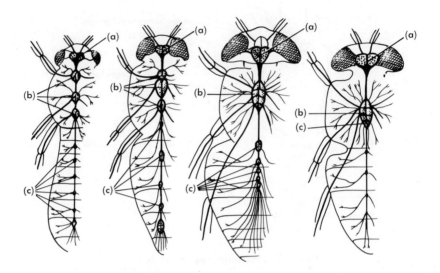

FIG. 39. Nervous systems of four species of flies (Diptera). The sequence is from the more primitive on the left to the more advanced on the right. The (a), "brain," remains separate; the thoracic ganglia (b) fuse into one unit; and the abdominal ganglia (c) fuse and unite with the thoracic.

toward complexes of stimuli, as in mating behavior; increased plasticity of responses; and new interindividual interactions leading toward group and social behavior.

### FUNCTIONS OF AN INTEGRATIVE SYSTEM

The sense organs receive information on changes that occur in the external environment, or, in some cases, from the internal environment of the organism. The nervous elements associated with the receptors then transmit this information, in coded form, to the central nervous system. It is in the nervous system that processing and integration take place, that significant environmental conditions are acted upon, and that some of the information is stored, i.e., memory.

The nervous system determines the behavior of the organism, but it does not act alone. Interacting with the nervous system are all the internal secretory glands (i.e., the endocrines) as well as the general physiological

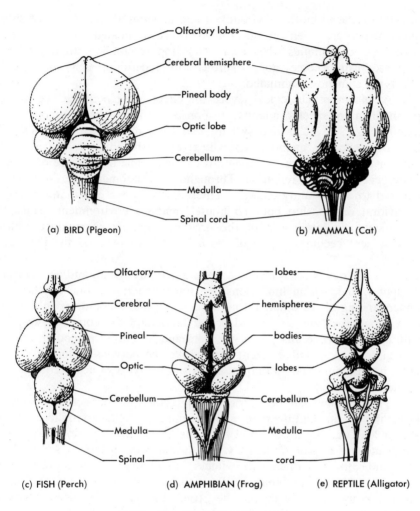

FIG. 40. Vertebrate brains.

state of the organism, such as the blood sugar concentration and other chemical factors.

In order for the animal to survive, its behavior must be constantly responsive not only to external stimuli, but also to internal requirements. The response to a particular external situation has to be appropriate to what has gone on before, which means that the integrative system must be able to accumulate the effects of prior experiences. At the lowest psychological levels, the effects of experience can consist of chemical changes directly produced by the environment and affecting the character of subsequent responses. When certain protozoans are stimulated repeatedly with a weak noxious stimulus, they eventually stop responding. In other cases, responses can become more vigorous with repetition, as if the stimulus effects are somehow summated.

At higher psychological levels, the effects of experience become apparent in more specific adaptive responses, and the effects become more long-lasting. An integrative system, therefore, must have a *memory*. In human psychology, memory generally refers to the ability to recall specific facts or experiences, but an integrative system must be capable of a much more general type of retention. Throughout development, the individual is exposed to a constantly changing environment and a constantly changing behavioral relationship between himself and his environment. Thus, the entire complex interaction of the organism and its environment during development becomes a part of the information stored by the integrative system.

An analogy is often made between a nervous system and an electronic computer, and, within limitations, the understanding of one assists in the understanding of the other. Information is fed into a computer in the form of a program of directions and coded facts, and the computer responds with an appropriate analysis of the data and an output of coded information in some new and different form. Like the nervous system, the computer has an input and an output, and a storage bank of acquired data, i.e., a "memory."

The analogy can be carried even further to the actual operations inside the organic and the man-made machine. A digital computer is simply a complex counting device, and it counts according to a binary system of numbers consisting of 1's and 0's. If a switch is on, it indicates a 1; if it is off, it indicates 0. With enough switches, any number can be represented by means of this simple binary system. Instead of switches, most modern computers use relays, vacuum tubes, transistors and other electrically controlled mechanisms, and the 1's and 0's are represented by the presence or absence of current in a particular circuit. Similarly in the nervous system, the nerve fibers are digital devices in their obedience to the all-or-none law, i.e., either there is an impulse present or there is no impulse present. This analogy was one of the factors that led to the formation of an entire field of study, i.e., *cybernetics*. This approach has been useful in clarifying some neurophysiological problems, and it has been especially valuable in developing computers and controlling systems.

One of the functions of nervous systems that has been exploited by computer engineers is *feedback*. An organism not only receives information about its external environment, but it has sensors that keep the nervous system informed of all the internal changes going on in connection with the response. A helmsman on a ship knows the direction in which he is moving from information supplied by his compass, but, as he changes course, he must also know how much he has altered the position of the rudder. He has, therefore, a special sensor that feeds back information on the extent of his ship's response and the position of the rudder. Well-organized integrative systems in animals possess a type of receptor known as a *proprioceptor*. This system of sense organs is located within the muscles and other body tissues, and it keeps the central nervous system informed about the state of contraction and activity of the entire organism.

The computer–nervous system analogy has its limitations and should not be carried too far, because there are some significant and fundamental differences in the two systems. If each neuron is considered the equivalent of a single binary digit in a computer, the nervous system of a mammal would possess in the order of several million such units, whereas the largest of our present computers contains only a few hundred thousand units. In level of complexity alone, the nervous system far exceeds that of any computer.

In addition to its resemblance to a digital computer, the nervous system can operate with graded responses, that is, responses that can change in magnitude continuously over a range. In this way, the nervous system operates like an analog computer. A digital computer simply counts numbers and is fundamentally an abacus, but an analog computer uses electrical circuits as equations and formulae. A voltmeter is a simple sort of analog computer, because it uses an equation (Ohm's Law, in this case) in the form of an equivalent electrical circuit. Of course much more complex equations can be set up and the answers displayed on meters or oscilloscope screens, but in each case, the mathematical operations are duplicated by analogous circuits. The degree to which the nervous system operates in this fashion is as yet poorly known, but it is evident that, at least at higher levels of organization, analog as well as digital functions take place. The progress of an impulse along the length of a nerve fiber is essentially digital, i.e., all-or-none. The transmission of an impulse across a synapse, however, involves graded responses and the integration of several inputs that eventually result in a decision to fire or not to fire a pulse.

Variability of response, and adaptive adjustment of response can be built into a machine, but even a simple nervous system can exhibit adaptive behavior and error correction that far outstrips the best of our present day computers. Theoretically, it is possible to build a machine that functions like a nervous system, but, by its very nature, it must operate on a level of organization different from that of an organic system.

Probably the most important single difference in the two systems is the fact that an organic integrative system is an ever-changing, dynamic process. Any given appropriate, adaptive activity of an animal that is observed at a particular time is only an instant along the continuum of development of that organism and the evolution of the species. Integration is developed, it exists at some level of organization at all times during the life of the organism, and it is continually changing with the growth of the individual and under the influence of environmental factors.

### NEUROLOGICAL BASIS OF BEHAVIOR

The *reflex* in its broad sense is generally considered to be the basic functional unit of a nervous system. At the simplest level (see, for example, the sponge in Fig. 41(A)), a reflex consists of a receptor cell that responds to some environmental stimulus, and the response of the receptor is directly transmitted to an effector cell that either contracts or secretes some chemical. This is known as "neuroid" conduction. Even among coelenterates (Fig. 41(B)), most reflexes involve at least three cells. The third element is a specialized cell with the ability to conduct an impulse over some distance. Most simple reflexes, then, have three cells: receptor, conductor (neuron), and effector.

Further specialization and additional cells are the components of reflexes in the vertebrates and the higher invertebrates. The usual situation includes not only a receptor and effector, but at least three intervening neurons (there are some instances of two neurons, but these are not common). A type of neural connection present in many invertebrates and occasionally in vertebrates is a reflex arc involving two neurons as shown in Fig. 41(C). In a typical three-neuron reflex, the receptor activates a sensory (afferent) neuron; the sensory neuron transmits its impulse at a connection point (synapse) to an association (internuncial) neuron; the association neuron activates a motor (efferent) neuron that stimulates the effector mechanism (Fig. 41(D)). The presence of separate sensory and motor neurons permits a considerable spatial separation of the receptor and effector organs, but the most important advance in integration is achieved by the association neuron. This cell not only activates many motor neurons, but it can pass the impulse on to other association neurons. The simple three-neuron reflex arc probably exists only as a theoretical unit, because the spread of the impulse to many other cells is almost inevitable. A comparison of animals at various levels of organization reveals that the main neurological differences are in the numbers and organization of the association neurons. The cerebral cortex of the human brain contains millions of neurons, most of which are of the association type.

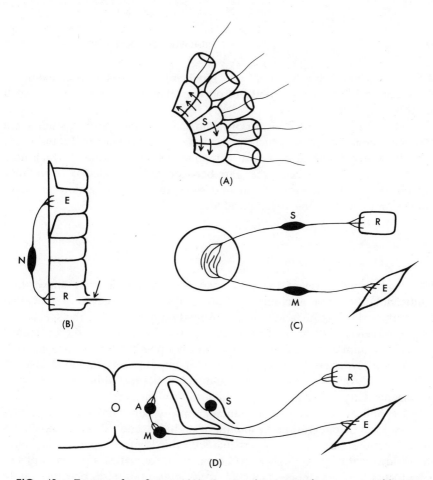

FIG. 41. Types of reflexes. (A) S—stimulus spreading to neighboring cells. (B) Arrow indicates receptor hair; R—receptor cell; N—neuron; E—contractile effector cell. (C) R—receptor cell; S—sensory neuron; M—motor neuron; E—effector. (D) A—association neuron.

One of the fundamental questions in the study of brain and behavior has always been: How does this complex of interconnected neurons determine behavior? Until recently, attempts to answer this question had not been very successful. Although a great deal had been learned about the function of neurons in the transmission of neural impluses, this knowledge shed little light on the basic problem of integrative function in the nervous system. In recent years, improvement in the techniques of electrophysiology have made it possible to study neural activity in intact and behaving animals, and to elicit organized behavior patterns by electrical stimulation of the brain of such animals. Furthermore, advances in biochemistry have led investigators to seek correlations between behavioral changes, such as those occurring during learning, and biochemical processes. For example, much research has been carried out on the relation of nucleic acids (such as RNA) to memory.

The findings of these electrophysiological and biochemical studies are extremely complex and frequently controversial and will not be discussed here. However it does appear that techniques are now available which may make it possible to bridge the gap between our knowledge of cellular organization and function and our understanding of organization and integration on the organismic, behavioral level.

### LEVELS OF INTEGRATION

A comparison of the protozoan and the coelenterate shows that multicellularity, with a connecting nerve net, has achieved a new and different level of organization. The coordination of parts and the specialization of sensory, effector, and connector units have provided the coelenterates with a number of behavioral capacities not possible for protozoans.

Radial symmetry is a basic plan that imposes certain limitations on behavior. Thus, the coelenterates and echinoderms, although far apart phylogenetically, exhibit many behavioral similarities.

Cephalization, and its concomitant sensory concentration, exemplifies another level of integration. Orientation, mobility, and all the complexities these functions entail are only possible with this kind of organization. With the endowment of these higher level behavioral capacities, the developmental process for the achievement of these capacities also becomes more complex. There is, therefore, a greater opportunity for stimulative environmental factors to influence behavioral development. Behavior becomes more adjustable and more responsive to environmental conditions.

After the evolution of primitive bilateral symmetry and cephalization, the animal kingdom split into two main lines, both of which developed a degree of centralization of integrative function. The invertebrates, culminating in the insects, possess a nervous system that is essentially a chain of ganglia with more or less autonomous control centers for each segment. The typical vertebrate nervous system is derived from a hollow, dorsal tube, with the anterior portion enlarged and modified into a brain.

The levels of integration achieved by these two evolutionary lines differ not only in degree but also in kind. The differences in structure are reflected in differences in behavioral capacities. More significantly, the developmental patterns of the two groups are different, and the importance of this fact will be discussed later. It is evident that the insect level of integration results in a highly stereotyped behavioral repertoire, whereas the vertebrate level is more plastic, especially among the higher vertebrates.

## Suggested Readings

Bennett, E. L., M. C. Diamond, D. Krech, and M. R. Rosenzweig. 1964. Chemical and Anatomical Plasticity of Brain. *Science,* 146: 610–619.

Grundfest, H. 1959. Evolution of conduction in the nervous system. *In Evolution of Nervous Control. Amer. Assoc. Adv. Sci.,* No. 52: 43–86.

Lashley, K. S. 1929. *Brain Mechanisms and Intelligence.* Reprinted edition, 1963. Dover Publications: New York.

Lashley, K. S. 1950. In search of the engram. *In Physiological Mechanisms in Animal Behaviour. Symp. Soc. Exp. Biol.,* No. 4: 454–482.

Passano, L. M. (ed.). 1965. Behavioral physiology of coelenterates. *Amer. Zoologist,* 5: 335–589.

Thompson, R. F. 1967. *Foundations of Physiological Psychology.* Harper & Row, Publishers: New York.

# 6    SPECIES-TYPICAL
  BEHAVIOR

A striking feature in the behavior of many species is the almost machinelike way with which the animals feed, fight, or mate. This feature is especially evident among insects and other arthropods, where complex sequences of activities take place in a specific, ordered, repetitive fashion. Such behavior patterns seem to appear with no apparent practice or experience. Every individual of the species appears to perform the same movement with virtually no variability. Even animals that have been isolated from their own kind since birth or hatching predictably behave in a stereotyped manner.

From the early days of animal behavior study, these stereotyped activities have been classified under terms such as tropisms, taxes, reflexes, instincts, and innate behaviors. The animal's response to a stimulus appears to be somehow built into its nervous system, and a given stimulus simply triggers a specific response. At least this is what *seems* to happen, but a careful analysis shows the situation to be considerably more complex.

## TAXES AND KINESES

Probably the most elementary behavior of an organism is an orientation with respect to a stimulus source. The animal may move or turn toward or away from the stimulus. Jacques Loeb called these orientations tropisms, but most later writers preferred the term *taxes* (*taxis,* sing.), in order to separate behavioral responses of animals from growth responses (tropisms) such as occur in plants. A taxis may be positive or negative with respect to the stimulus, i.e., the animal turns toward or away. Thus, we can speak of a positive phototaxis as an orientation toward a light source and a negative phototaxis as an orientation away from the light. Similarly, the terms chemotaxis (chemical), geotaxis (gravity), thigmotaxis (contact), rheotaxis (current), etc. are commonly used.

Some important features of a taxis are its automatic character, simplicity of integration, and low standing in the scale of psychological levels. In a bilaterally symmetrical animal, such as an earthworm, equal stimulation of light receptors on both sides results in equal excitation of the locomotor musculature so that the animal moves in a straight line away from the light source. When the receptors on the left are stimulated more strongly by a light beam, the muscles on the opposite, right side contract more strongly, and the animal turns away from the light. A similar situation can be demonstrated in a flatworm in which a unilateral stimulation by an attractive chemical, such as meat juice, causes the muscles on that side to contract, and the animal orients in the direction of the stimulus. A positively phototactic insect that has been blinded in one eye will walk around in circles, always turning away from the blind side. When an animal is faced with any directional stimulus, a tactic response enables it to orient with respect to the stimulus source, and, by maintaining equal stimulus intensities on the left and right receptors, it will then move toward or away from the stimulus.

Many factors can modify and even reverse the tactic response. In most cases, a low-intensity stimulus evokes a positive taxis, and the same stimulus at a high intensity will produce a negative taxis. Earthworms, for example, will move away from a strong light, but toward a weak one, and, in many species, chemotaxes can be reversed from positive to negative simply by increasing the concentration of the chemical. Internal and external conditions can change the direction of a taxis, weaken it, or inhibit it altogether.

A taxis is often called a *forced response,* in the sense that the organism is governed by the directional nature of the stimulus in a mechanical way, just as pressing a switch in an electrical circuit turns on an appropriate light bulb. Taxes appear to be present in all metazoa and are usually readily identifiable among the invertebrates and some vertebrate larvae and embryos. It is often difficult to demonstrate a pure tactic response in an adult vertebrate.

A taxis must include some relationship between the directionality of the stimulus and the orientation of the organism. Only a bilaterally symmetrical animal, with differentiated left and right sides, can exhibit a taxis. However, many protozoans that are not bilaterally symmetrical show an orientation and can move toward or away from a source of stimulation. Here a different orienting mechanism is involved, called a *kinesis*. In its simplest form, *Euglena* moves toward a light source by wandering about until it is oriented so that its light-sensitive stigma receives the strongest illumination. (See Fig. 42.)

A typical example of a kinesis is exhibited by the sow bug or wood louse. In a lighted area, the sow bug simply walks faster than in a shaded area. At low-intensity illumination, locomotion slows down or may stop temporarily. Under such conditions, several sow bugs will eventually collect in a shaded spot. Some types of kineses result from a differential rate of turning, and thus the animals will have a greater probability of orienting toward or away from a stimulus source.

Like taxes, kineses are forced responses in the sense that the stimulus intensity controls the behavior of the organism. In both cases, the directionality of the stimulus energy is responded to in a direct fashion, although a taxis orientation involves a higher level of sensory and central nervous organization than does a kinesis.

## COMPASS AND OTHER ORIENTATIONS

Ants that follow trails to and from their nest use a variety of cues, but chief among these is sunlight. Ants, as well as many other species of animals, will often orient themselves and move in some direction *with respect to* the source of light. Such instances of orientation are called compass reactions, and these are clearly different from ordinary taxes because the animal orients itself at some specific angle to the stimulus source, not only directly at or away from the source.

One of the most striking examples of sun compass orientation was demonstrated by experiments with starlings. Under captive conditions, these migratory birds will still orient and flutter in the appropriate direction, but only as long as the sun is visible. Under artificial conditions, their orientation can be shifted by changing the apparent direction of the sun or by placing them on altered schedules of day and night. (See Fig. 43.)

It is apparent that another kind of orientation must be present to

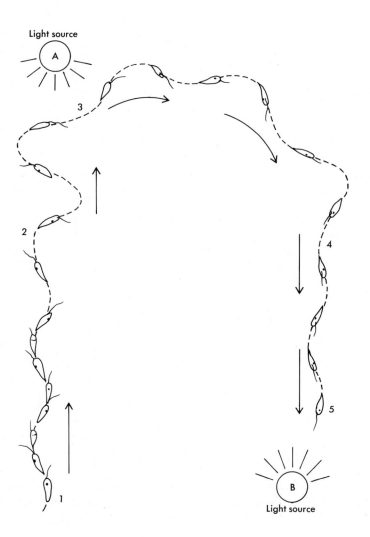

FIG. 42. The phototactic orientation of the plant flagellate *Euglena. Euglena* swims in its characteristic spiral motion toward the source of light (A). Upon reaching point 2, the light is changed to (B). Because of the asymmetry of its light receptor organ, the *Euglena* eventually changes direction and swims toward the new light source. (After G.S. Fraenkel and D.L. Gunn, *The Orientation of Animals,* Dover Publications, 1961.)

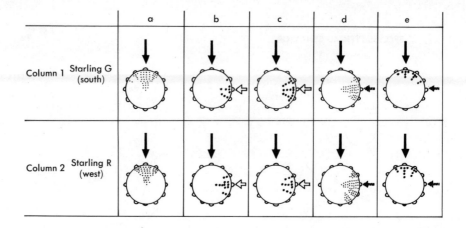

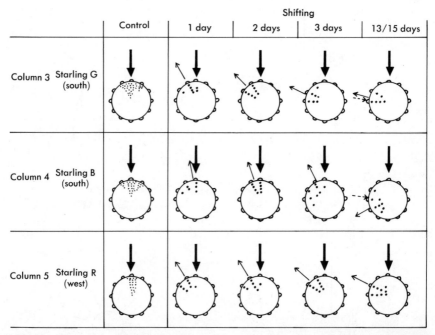

FIG. 43. The sun-oriented directional choice of a trained starling is closely correlated with the phase of the sun or an artificially imposed light-dark cycle. In the circular diagrams each dot represents one unrewarded choice. In the upper five columns the solid inward arrows indicate the training direction. In the first two horizontal columns two birds (G and R) were trained to the south and west respectively (a). Then their light-dark schedule was delayed 6 hours and after 12 to 18 days they were tested (b). This new direction persisted even after 3 to 28 days of constant light (c). Then they were retrained during an artificial day (d), see the striped arrow, and again tested 8 to 17 days after they were returned to natural light (e). The shift of orientation after placing on an altered light-dark schedule is gradual (columns 3, 4, and 5). Here the light cycle is shifted 6 hours ahead. (After P. Marler and W. J. Hamilton, *Mechanisms of Animal Behavior*, John Wiley & Sons, 1966.)

account for the consistency of the sun compass reactions. It is remarkable that the animals in these experiments maintain the same compass direction at different times of the day, yet the sun appears to move across the sky. This means, therefore, that the animals possess a temporal orientation, often called a *biological clock*. Many animals show patterns of behavior that wax and wane at different times of the 24-hour day according to some more or less regular rhythms. Such *circadian* rhythms will, in many cases, continue and persist even after the animals are placed in artificial surroundings where the environmental conditions are uniform or changed to some abnormal time schedule. In most experimental work, it can be shown that these rhythms are developed and controlled by the rhythmicity of the natural environment, but there is some evidence that fundamental biochemical events have a rhythmicity. The problem of the development of circadian rhythms in animals is an active field of research, and evidence seems to support the idea of direct or indirect control by external stimuli.

### LEVELS OF ORIENTATION

A significant concept emerges from a comparative study of orientation in various animals. Although orientation, in the sense of moving or turning in relation to some directional source of stimulation, is common to all animals, there are many qualitatively different kinds of orientation. Orientation involves some degree of motor coordination and, therefore, some degree of integration. A compass reaction requires a higher level of integration than a taxis, and compass reactions include organismic properties not present in organisms at lower levels of integration. However, animals that exhibit compass reactions may also show taxis behavior at different stages of their development.

The simplest and most primitive kind of orientation is one in which the organism orients or moves toward or away from the stimulus souce. The intensity of the stimulus determines the response to be either an approach or a withdrawal. An amoeba, for example, will respond to a weak alkali by moving toward the source, whereas it will move away if the concentration of the chemical is increased. A sow bug will orient toward a weak light source, but away from a strong one.

At higher levels of nervous organization, the quality of the stimulus begins to play a more important role, and the orientation behavior involves more complex neural functions than can be accounted for by kineses, taxes, and compass reactions. Even the simplest reflexes involve association neurons, whose presence makes an intricate interconnection possible among many reflexes. Furthermore, these association neurons provide the capability for a more flexible, adaptive behavior that is much more responsive to subtle environmental changes and allows a wider range of behavioral adjustments. Thus, in the orientation of a migrating bird, although it may be possible to identify some tactic components in its movements, the total behavior involves a much higher level of nervous organization than can be accounted for by taxes or simple reflexes.

### INTERACTIONS AND COMMUNICATION

Orientation in animals includes much more than orientation to inanimate objects and sources of stimuli. Animals orient with respect to other animals, and such behavior is usually termed *interaction*. Animal interactions can exist between members of the same species, as in reproductive and social behavior, or between individuals of different species, as in predator-prey relations.

The barracuda is a well-known predatory fish that feeds primarily on schooling vegetarians such as mullet or herring. A complex of interactions can be observed between the predator and its prey. The swimming movements of the prey animals are seen by the predator, and their vibrations are detected by the barracuda's lateral line system. The barracuda is detected in the same way by the mullet. The stimuli involved in this interaction arise primarily from each animal's basic locomotor activity, and vision, sound detection, and, possibly, chemical senses are involved. The responses of the prey animals are not specific for barracudas, but are essentially the same for any predator or any object that resembles a predator. The action of the barracuda is also nonspecific, and it will attack a large variety of similar prey, even crude man-made lures that resemble small fish. It is evident that this interaction must require only a relatively low level of integration, because the stimuli are nonspecific and no highly specialized forms of behavior are involved.

By contrast, the interactions among members of a colony of monkeys are on a much higher level. The individuals go through a long period of development of socialization. Mother-infant relations, scuffles among juveniles, and other interactions affect the way in which the individual behaves as an adult. The interactions themselves are not only specialized, but they involve primitive forms of symbolic communication.

It is evident that interactions are of many different kinds, i.e., levels, and some of these can be termed communications. Simply stated, one organism emits some form of energy, and another organism receives the energy and reacts to it. In the case of a protozoan emitting some chemicals that are normal by-products of its metabolism, there may be some forced responses by other protozoa as a result of the chemical effects of these by-products. This is clearly an interaction on a low level of integration.

The schooling behavior of fishes is based primarily upon the visual stimuli of one moving fish upon another, although acoustic and chemical stimuli also play a role. The stimuli emitted are broad in the sense of encompassing a wide spectrum of intensities and other qualities. The responses are nonspecialized locomotor orientations. In this interaction, the level of integration is still low, but distinctly higher and different from that of interacting protozoa.

A higher level of interaction is exemplified by animals that produce a specific stimuli, usually from specialized organs, e.g., ants exuding particular chemicals that mark their trails; fish flashing specific color patterns during territorial and reproductive behavior; dogs, porpoises, or other mammals uttering cries associated with distress. These stimuli are generally responded to in some highly specific fashion by the receiver animals, and, therefore, such stimuli can be termed *signals*. The term *communication* should be reserved for interactions on this level.

Among many mammals, especially the primates, communication achieves a significantly higher level. Interactions among monkeys are highly dependent upon their social environment. A monkey reared under artificial conditions and with no contact with other monkeys will never develop socially, will not interact normally when placed with other monkeys, and will not develop normal reproductive behavior. For this level of interaction, higher integrative functions involving the effects of prior social experience are required.

In any comparison of interactions and communications in different species, it becomes important to understand the level of organization of each and the qualitative differences between them. In order to make such comparisons, therefore, one must keep phyletic and structural differences in mind, as well as the ways in which the interactions have developed in the individual.

### REPRODUCTIVE BEHAVIOR

It is obvious that for a species to survive its members must reproduce, and in all, except for some of the most primitive invertebrates, sexual reproduction predominates. Even in protozoans occasional conjugation with a mixing of genetic materials is necessary for the strains to survive. A fundamental feature of animal behavior, therefore, is the synchronous production of gametes by individuals of opposite sex. All activities that precede and lead to the actual fusion of the gametes fall into the general category of reproductive behavior. If there is any parental care of the young, this behavior is also reproductive in a broad sense.

In any comparison of reproductive behavior among various animals, it is evident that the activities characterizing different phyletic levels are based upon different levels of organization. A few examples will be considered, although it should be noted that in many instances the details of the interactions and their development are not completely known.

The mechanisms by means of which two paramecia are attracted to each other are unknown. Some chemical stimuli are probably involved, and, as in any protozoan, the effects are directly upon the entire cell, and the responses are controlled by the quality and quantity of the stimulus. In such cases, the level of integration involved in the conjugation process must be extremely low.

Reproductive behavior among annelid worms is much more complex and involves the full utilization of all the sensory systems and central integration that the organism possesses. The reproduction of the Caribbean fire-worm (*Odontoscillus*) is a particularly dramatic example. This small worm, a relative of the common marine sand worm (*Neanthes*), grows to perhaps an inch in length and spends its time burrowing in the silt of the bays of most of the West Indies. Predictably, on the fifth night after an August full moon, the reproductive forms of these worms come out of their burrows and swim to the surface of the water. The timing of this behavior is controlled by a variety of factors, including day length, temperature, and tidal rhythms. On such a night, there is about an hour between the setting of the sun and the rising of the moon. Twilight is short in the tropics, and during this period the only illumination is starlight, if the night is cloudless. Light, however, is provided by the worms themselves. At this time, the only time in their lives, they become phosphorescent, and the water surface sparkles as if with thousands of tiny, greenish, blinking Christmas tree lights. The lights of the two sexes are different: Males blink on and off about once or twice a second; females turn on a brighter light that remains steady for at least ten seconds. When a female lights up, males converge on her, blinking as they swim. Eventually there is a tiny phosphorescent explosion at the center of which the worms whirl about in tight circles, releasing a glowing cloud of eggs and sperm. After these nuptials, the light fades out, the worms sink down, and most of them probably die shortly thereafter.

Complex though it seems, the regulation of the behavior of the fire-worm is based upon rigidly developed responses to a sequence of stimuli, some from the environment and some from other worms. The simplicity of the central nervous system does not allow for much variability or adjustment of the behavior pattern, and sensory control predominates.

The reproductive behavior of many fishes is more variable, more dependent upon central integration, and includes a significant period of preparatory activity. In a species of tidal zone fish known as a goby (*Bathygobius soporator*), the individuals develop territorial behavior before achieving sexual maturity. This behavior consists of defending some small area, usually where shelter (e.g., an empty shell, a crevice, or even a beer can) is available. Territorial defense is manifested by a darkening of the body colors and gaping and throat-puffing movements toward intruding gobies. With sexual maturity, the territorial behavior becomes more intense, especially in males. Visual cues appear to predominate in such encounters, although sometimes the combatants will actually bite each other. The larger individual, and the one who has held the territory longest, will usually win out, while the intruder decamps. If, however, the intruder is a female gravid with eggs, the behavior of the territory-holding male changes drastically. Stimulated by both visual and chemical cues, he changes to a light body color with a black chin and proceeds to dart about the female with vigorous fanning movements of the body and tail. (See Fig. 44.)

Some form of pre-mating or courtship behavior is common among many animals, both vertebrates and higher invertebrates. An important function of courtship is discrimination of species and sex through this sequence of interactions. Another function of courtship is to mutually stimulate the two participants so that the pair can be maintained until the proper physiological state for mating is achieved by both.

In the goby, the interactions of stimuli between a pair of individuals during courtship involve several sensory modalities, all of which are important in maintaining the pair. The female's behavior is to hold her ground as the male approaches. When she is gravid, she exudes a chemical that stimulates the male to more intense courting behavior. The male's fanning is accompanied by low-intensity grunting noises that attract and stimulate the female. The stimuli from one partner arouse the other reciprocally, and eventually the pair move into the shelter the male has been defending all along. The female lays adherent eggs on the inside surfaces of the shelter, and the male simultaneously releases sperm. Once the female has released her eggs, she leaves the shelter, and the male remains with the eggs, guarding and fanning them until they hatch.

Several experiments demonstrate the controlling mechanisms and level of integration involved in the reproductive behavior of the goby. The presence of male sex hormones, secreted by the testes, are essential for adequate territorial behavior. Castrated males do not defend their territory, but will attempt to court males and females indiscriminately. The lack of hormone possibly affects the sensitivity of their olfactory system in some way, so that they are no longer capable of discriminatory behavior, al-

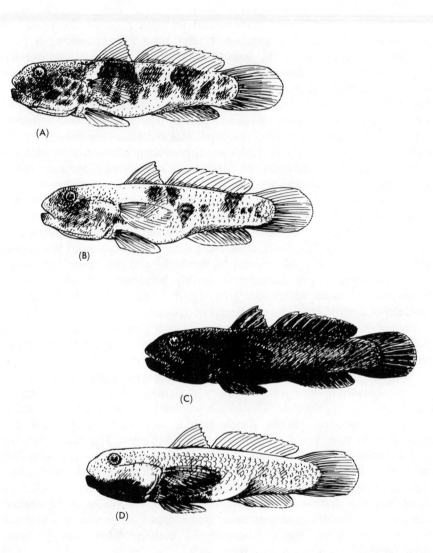

FIG. 44. In the goby, *Bathygobius,* the male (A) and female (B) are normally very similar in color pattern. When a male encounters an intruding male in his territory, however, he turns dark (C) and attacks the intruder. If the intruder happens to be a mature female, his color pattern turns predominantly light except for a dark chin (D), and courtship behavior follows. (After W. N. Tavolga, "Reproductive Behavior in the Gobiid Fish, *Bathygobius soporator, Bull. Amer. Mus. Nat. Hist.,* vol. 104, 1954.)

though such individuals will go through complete spawning behavior with a gravid female. The eggs, in this case, would not be fertilized. Males with their nostrils plugged or olfactory organs cauterized cease all courting behavior, but will continue to defend their shelters vigorously. A mature, gravid female will, if not given a choice, spawn with a young male, but in this case, she deposits eggs irregularly both inside and outside the shelter. She will also often eat her own eggs, and the young male releases sperm irregularly and, usually, unsuccessfully. A mature, experienced male is evidently necessary to stimulate the female's behavior adequately.

Mating behavior in mammals requires a long period of socialization. Effects of experience can even override hormonal control. Male cats that are castrated after having had considerable experience in copulation will lose their copulatory behavior gradually. Usually those activities that require the highest degree of arousal tend to cease first. Cats that are castrated before attaining puberty, or after only a small amount of sexual experience, exhibit virtually no sex behavior. In many mammals, especially primates, normal reciprocal stimulations between mother and young, and among litter mates, are essential for the development of normal sex behavior.

Reproductive behavior as a general category can be characterized as the series of activities that lead to reproduction of the species. It is important to understand, however, that reproductive behavior differs at various phyletic levels and involves different levels of integration. The developmental mechanisms at these levels differ not only in degree but in kind.

### SOCIAL BEHAVIOR

Many species of animals tend to form groups. This grouping, which may be sporadic or obligate, has some selective, evolutionary advantages, but the groupings range from loose, temporary aggregations to tight, physiologically and morphologically maintained social structures. The social insects, e.g., bees and ants, and many mammals are considered to be examples of highly socialized forms, and comparisons are often made between the social structures of the two. Such comparisons are often made without regard to the vast differences in levels of organization and the fundamental differences in the pathways of development of social behavior.

A most intensively studied species of social insect has been the tropical American army ant (*Eciton*). These ants form huge colonies of hundreds of thousands of individuals, most of whom cling together to erect a living mound in the center of which is the queen. Irregular columns of raiders move out and bring back booty as food for the colony. The booty consists mainly of other insects or even small rodents. The main colony mass takes up a temporary residence in a hollow log, under an overhanging bush, hidden in the underbrush with its numerous raiding columns radiating out like tentacles. At certain periods in the life of a colony, there is a night-time emigration of the entire bivouac, usually following the trail of one of the major raiding columns. Such *nomadic* emigrations continue nightly for up to a few weeks, and then the entire colony goes into a *statary* phase, during which most of the colony members remain clustered together and the raiding columns are sparse.

Each worker in the colony stimulates other workers, mainly through chemical and tactile senses. Each worker is himself stimulated by other workers. The queen stimulates the workers, but she is also stimulated by them. The complexity of interactions has been called *reciprocal stimulation* by T. C. Schneirla, and this reciprocity is central to the control of the cyclic behavior. The queen is the focus of chemical excitation, and the workers cluster about her closely. The workers farther away are stimulated both by the queen's secretions and by her aroused court. Food also has an excitatory effect, and raiding parties returning with booty stimulate increased activity and raiding by other colony members. The queen's primary function is to lay eggs, and when these hatch into helpless larvae, the larvae also have an effect on the behavior of the workers. Workers feed the larvae excess food from the raiding parties. Each colony member is a sort of walking restaurant, doling out morsels and receiving morsels, exchanging food and excitatory secretions constantly. The larvae are expecially stimulating, and also constantly hungry, and thus the entire colony becomes stimulated to a high pitch of raiding activity. This produces the nomadic period (Fig. 45).

As the larvae mature and begin to go into the nonfeeding pupa stage, the activity of the colony decreases. The colony goes into its statary phase, but the active nomadic phase has had its effect upon the queen, who produces a large batch of eggs. About the time the new workers emerge from their pupal cases and begin to feed, the new brood of eggs begins to hatch. The emergence of the callow workers and the new larvae stimulates the colony into a new burst of nomadic and raiding activity. The timing is right, because the callows do not participate in the raiding but consume much food. Thus, the colony recycles and restimulates itself, with the queen's egg production rate acting as a sort of clock.

The queen's clock, however, is not independent and self-running, because she, in turn, depends upon the food and stimulation of the workers. Furthermore, weather conditions and food availability play an important role, and, at certain seasons, the brood produced is small in relation to the food supply. Such well-fed larvae become sexually mature males and fe-

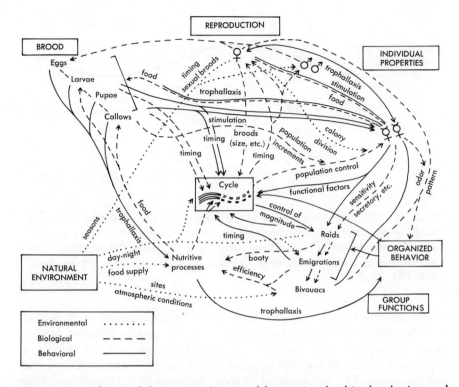

**FIG. 45.** A schema of the principal types of factors involved in developing and maintaining the cyclic behavior pattern of species in *Eciton* and certain other genera of Doryline ants. The major sources of factors are indicated marginally in rectangles. The principal interrelationships demonstrated among these factors are indicated by appropriately directed arrows. Arrows also indicate the bearing of these major factors upon the functional cycle of the colony, represented by a sine wave in the center of the diagram. (After T.C. Schneirla, "Theoretical Considerations of Cyclic Processes in Doryline Ants," *Proc. Amer. Philos. Soc.,* vol. 101, 1957.)

males. As the colony grows and fertile females survive, a division may take place, with a new young queen emigrating with her entourage of workers (Fig. 46).

However, no matter how complex the control of social life of the army ant may seem to be, the regulating mechanisms are essentially of an organic, metabolic nature. Individual behavior is stereotyped, limited, and rigidly controlled by a small number of stimulus variables. Even during embryonic and larval development, the environmental control is extremely limiting, so that, no matter what the individual's potential might be, an ant

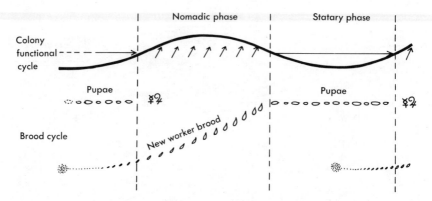

FIG. 46.    The interaction of the entire complex of factors shown in Fig. 45
result in an alternation of migratory, nomadic periods with statary periods
in which the colony is less active. (After T.C. Schneirla, "Theoretical Considerations of Cyclic Processes in Doryline Ants," *Proc. Amer. Philos. Soc.*,
Vol. 101, 1957.)

cannot develop behaviorally into anything but the stereotype of its species.

By contrast, a mammal goes through a completely different kind of
social development. All mammals are social animals to some degree, at
least to the extent of a complex series of interactions between the mother
and her young. The development of social behavior in the domestic cat has
been investigated intensively. Initially, a new-born kitten operates primarily on the basis of simple attractive or aversive, tactual and chemical
stimuli. As its eyes open and its locomotor coordination improves, reciprocal stimulation between the mother and the kitten increases in scope and
importance. The activity of other kittens of the litter provides new stimuli
of a complex nature, and higher integrative processes begin to predominate
in the development. Experiences beyond the simple metabolic effects influence the kitten, and it integrates these experiences into its development as
an individual. The final result is a highly variable and plastic behavior as
compared to that of an ant. The behavior of the cat when it reaches sexual
maturity is molded by its experiences as a kitten, but behavioral maturation
does not stop here. A mother cat with her first litter is not nearly as
efficient in her brood care as one who has had several litters. As in the
function of an ant colony, reciprocal stimulation plays an important role,
but, unlike the ant colony, the reciprocal stimulations among the members
of a cat family are on a significantly higher level of neural and behavioral
organization.

As in the study of interaction and communication, it is evident that many different kinds of group behavior operate on different levels of organization and utilize different developmental pathways. Any understanding of comparative social studies of different species requires more than just a description and a labeling of the behavior; it requires an approach to the question: "How does the behavior develop?"

## INSTINCTIVE BEHAVIOR

An old and recurring problem in animal behavior has been the concept of "instinct" and how to define it. Traditionally, an instinct is thought of as an automatic response, an inherited or innate behavior, an unlearned behavior that is built-in as part of the structure of the organism. In performing an instinctive act, the animal is considered to behave like a machine that can do only the things it is built to do. Pressing the correct switch (stimulating the appropriate receptor) will activate specific preformed circuits (reflexes), and the appropriate wheels will turn (an instinctive behavior is evoked). Numerous mechanical models of instinctive behavior have been proposed in the past, and one, devised by K. Z. Lorenz, postulated the presence of action-specific energy. This neural form of potential energy was conceived as being locked up within the central nervous system, and, upon the stimulation of the appropriate receptors, released by a triggering mechanism through the neural pathways to the effectors. Many ethologists who are followers of Lorenz's instinct theories adhere to the concept of an innate releasing mechanism (IRM) for each instinctive act, and some current literature utilizes the term *releaser* for an environmental stimulus that evokes a particular innate behavior. Implicit in the use of the word releaser is the acceptance of the idea that the behavior is preformed as a neural circuit. The appropriate stimulus opens the doorway, and the behavioral energy rushes out. For a detailed exposition of the early ethological theories, see N. Tinbergen's book: *The Study of Instinct* (1951). Many investigators however, do not accept some of these concepts, and there have been numerous strongly critical appraisals of this instinctivist approach, notably by D. S. Lehrman, H. Moltz, and T. C. Schneirla (see bibliography).

In essence, the instinct concept is an oversimplification, and it substitutes labels for explanations. Calling a behavior an instinct explains nothing, and the separation of behavior into innate (inherited) and acquired (learned) is a revival of the nature vs. nurture controversy. In specific instances where instinctive behavior has been studied in a developmental fashion, it can be seen that each seemingly innate activity passes through stages of development and, at each stage, is affected by the organism's experience with its environment. Even an animal isolated from birth from its fellows has certain experiences with its environment and with itself, and these experiences mold the development of its behavior. This view is in complete agreement with the modern concepts of heredity that consider the phenotype of the individual the end product of interaction of the genotype with its environment. The inherited DNA of the individual determines the probabilities that in a given environment the development of the organism will proceed along certain pathways.

An excellent example of the complexity of factors underlying a species-typical behavior is to be found in the analysis of maternal feeding behavior in the ring dove. The male and female of this species court, build a nest, and lay their eggs like other birds. However, feeding of the young birds involves the regurgitation by the parent of a substance called crop milk. The behavior pattern is quite complex and seems highly purposive. The adult bird walks over to the squab, grasps its bill, and regurgitates the crop milk. Superficial analysis might lead one to characterize this behavior as innate or instinctive. However, a series of studies by Lehrman and his associates have shown that this behavior is the result of a complex interaction of the animal's species-typical structure with its species-typical environment.

Crop milk production depends upon the secretion, by the pituitary gland, of a hormone called *prolactin*. However, crop milk is not produced all the time but only when "needed". This does not involve "purpose" on the parent's part, but simply the fact that the presence of its mate causes the pituitary gland to secrete the hormone. Because the presence of the mate is part of the animal's species-typical experience prior to the hatching of the young, crop milk will, of necessity, be available for the young when needed.

Furthermore, the apparently purposive feeding behavior by the parent appears to depend upon a complex series of interactions between the parent and the young. Developmental studies of the behavior have shown that a young bird with its newly hatched brood of squabs is originally quite ineffective in feeding them, and that the squabs are not very efficient at finding food. With repeated experience the behavior becomes relatively stereotyped and efficient. Lehrman has shown, for example, that injection of prolactin is far more likely to elicit proper feeding behavior in adult birds who have previously raised young than in birds with no prior maternal experience.

Finally, Lehrman was able to explain the gradual weaning of the young from crop milk to the kinds of food eaten by the parents. As the young get larger, they provide stimuli which affect the endocrine system and cause a gradual reduction in the production of crop milk. As a result, the contents of the crop come gradually to include less crop milk and more seed, grains, and other adult foods. Thus, the proportion of crop milk in each feeding decreases gradually until the young are being fed only on the kinds of food the parents eat, and soon start feeding themselves.

Thus, what looks like a mysterious type of "instinctive" or inborn behavior is shown to result from the interaction of a variety of factors: structural, hormonal, neural, sensory, experiential, etc. Given a species-typical environment and a species-typical structure, the development of a purposive behavior follows naturally. The developmental process is a complex one, however, involving the integration of structural, hormonal, neural, sensory, and experiential factors.

In his studies on the tropical American army ants, T. C. Schneirla showed that the cyclical migrations of these huge colonies were controlled by a complex interaction of stimuli (see above).

Development of a behavior does not begin at hatching or birth, but has its primordia in the embryo, just as structural characteristics do. Quantitative and developmental studies of stereotyped behavior demonstrate clearly that a significant degree of variability exists in all cases, and this variability contributes some plasticity to the behavior pattern as a whole. Stereotyped behavior, therefore, is a relative term, and an investigation of the variability of this type of behavior is as important to an explanation of its mechanisms as a description of the usual sequence of events.

The dangers of making unwarranted, a priori assumptions was pointed out in an earlier chapter, and nowhere is this danger better exemplified than in the study of instinctive behavior. It is easy to fall into the trap of drawing a line between innate and acquired behavior and proceed from there into a labyrinth of terminology. A valid question is not whether a behavior is innate or acquired, but, rather, how does it develop? What are the factors that elicit and control its expression?

According to this view, what, then, is an instinct? An instinctive behavior can be defined as an activity that develops as the animal grows up in its normal environment; it is a behavior that is typical of the species and, as such, is probably adaptive and important for the survival of the individual and the species; it is more or less stereotyped, i.e., there is relatively little variability in its performance; once developed, it is resistant to alteration; in many of its characteristics, it resembles species-typical structure.

But have we really defined instinct? With very little stretching, the above definition could apply to virtually any behavior in any animal. Many kinds of learned behavior, even in man, could qualify under the above definition. With the modern approach toward an appreciation of levels of organization and an epigenetic behavioral concept, the notion of a separate category of behavior as instinctive becomes superfluous. What might qual-

ify as an instinctive behavior of a flatworm is quite different from what
might qualify as a human instinct. The notion of a dichotomy of behavior
is a very pervasive one, and, like early Lamarckian theories of evolution,
will probably persist for years to come. Careful students of behavior, however, are coming to realize that there are categories of behavior, but not the
simple acquired-innate alternatives. The categories are natural ones, based
upon phylogenetic differences and levels of organization. Unfortunately,
these categories are not clear-cut, and comparative behavioral analysis
necessitates rigorous experiments and complex techniques.

### EVOLUTIONARY DEVELOPMENT OF BEHAVIOR

The unifying thread in any comparative study, be it morphology
or behavior, structure or function, is the concept of evolution. This is the
inevitable context within which much of biological science operates. The
fact that organic evolution has taken place was clearly demonstrated by
Charles Darwin. His idea of natural selection as the means by which diversi-
fication and specialization occur still stands, although our present understanding of its complexities is considerably improved. The chief advance
that has been made since Darwin's day is the inclusion of the science of
genetics in the modern synthetic theory of evolution. We now have some
understanding of how mutations arise, how they affect the development of
the organism, and how they behave in populations. Thus, we are now in a
position to offer explanations of some evolutionary mechanisms on the
molecular level. As a result of the unification of many aspects of biological
sciences, we are now able to discuss organismic, behavioral problems in
relation to evolution.

Evolution is essentially a historical study, and the evidence that is
required for it consists of data about past events from which phylogenetic
relationships are deduced. Evolutionary evidence comes to us primarily in
the form of fossilized remains. From these, coupled with geological information, we can study the evolution of structural characteristics, their relation in time, and sometimes even the environmental conditions influencing
selection. Direct evidence of the evolution of behavior is sadly lacking,
except for occasional behavioral fossils such as footprints, burrows, and
toothmarks. From an examination of structure, however, it is often possible to deduce some facts about the behavior of extinct species. The structure and behavior of existing, related forms can also assist deductions of
the behavior of extinct forms.

A study of the jaw suspensions of fishes reveals the evolution of feeding
mechanisms, and investigations of the teeth of ancestral horses unfold a

story of changes in feeding behavior. The teeth of the horse changed from sharp, pointed molars for chewing tough, leafy vegetation to broader, more complex grinding surfaces for eating grass as shown in Fig. 47(A). Locomotor patterns of fishes, quadrupeds (Fig. 47(B)), birds, and other forms can be reconstructed on the basis of fossilized skeletons, together with information on present species. More complex behavior, such as courtship and territoriality, cannot be deduced from historical relics, and the animal behaviorist is forced to rely on studies of modern species entirely. He is, however, immeasurably aided by the information from the comparative anatomist on the phylogenetic relationships of the species he studies.

The concept of levels of organization follows morphological and phylogenetic levels closely, and there are profound psychological differences of a qualitative nature between animals at terminal branches of the phylogenetic tree. Organisms such as insects and mammals differ as much behaviorally as they do morphologically.

Some significant divergences between psychological levels and phylogeny do exist. Modern echinoderms are behaviorally closer to coelenterates than they are to the chordates in spite of the fact that there is an ancient common ancestry between echinoderms and chordates. In this situation, it is evident that radial symmetry, even though it is secondary, is associated with a noncentralized, low level of organization.

When an investigator observes that two animals of different species behave in a similar fashion, he cannot assume any relationship exists until he examines the underlying morphological basis for the similarity. Even then, he can only deduce that some relationship exists, but he is unable to say what historical, i.e., evolutionary, pathways led to the similarity. This he can do only with the aid of data of a historical, i.e., paleontological nature.

This problem is not unique to the student of animal behavior. Any biologist who studies physiological processes in existing species is faced with the unavailability of historical data directly bearing upon his problem. The comparative anatomist or embryologist who compares a fish, frog, cat, and man is not studying a historical sequence but is looking at end products of various branches of phylogeny. It is difficult, if not impossible, to project evolutionary pathways either forward or backward in time, because of the intrinsic unpredictability of evolution. To complicate the picture further, parallelism and convergence are extremely common and produce resemblances that are not the result of phylogenetic relationships. The plasticity of behavioral traits makes them prone to manifest these unrelated similarities to an even greater degree than do structural characteristics.

Each species is adapted through evolution to a specific complex of environmental conditions in which it is most likely to survive and repro-

(A) TEETH

(B) LIMBS

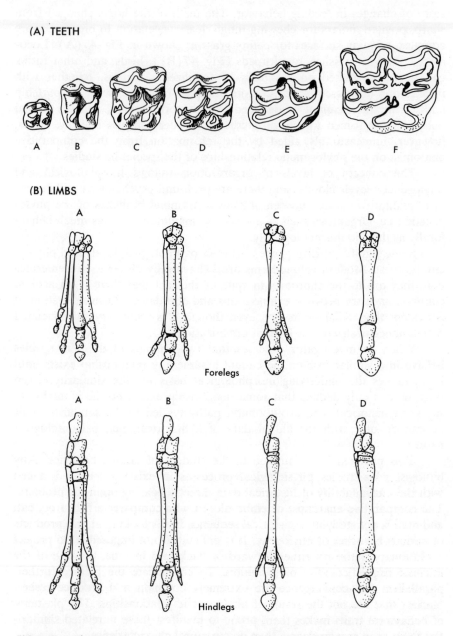

FIG. 47.  The sequence of evolutionary development of the modern horse from the Eocene *Eohippus*. (After A.S. Romer, *Vertebrate Paleontology*, University of Chicago Press, 1966.)

duce. The selection of this *ecological niche* is, to some extent, governed by the conditions in which the animal finds itself upon birth or hatching, but to a great extent it is dependent upon the behavior of the individual. It is the individual that locates situations where food is optimal, where temperature is comfortable, and where stressful stimuli are at a minimum. In two closely related subspecies of deer mice (*Peromyscus*), one tends to live in a grassy habitat, whereas the other selects a woodland area; this selection can be tested using single animals. The selection of a niche is not purposive in that the animal is not cognizant of the future consequences of its actions, but the process of evolution has produced a particular developmental pattern such that the organism is most likely to become attracted to an environment in which the chances of survival are greatest. The plasticity of behavior, even among stereotyped forms, allows the organism to adjust its actions when faced with changing situations.

In many cases, the action of an individual is affected by the behavior of other members of the species. In a school of fish, each animal maintains a specific distance between itself and its fellows. The cyclic raiding of legionary ants are the result of the interaction among the individuals of the colony and their queen. In some social groupings, the entire group or colony behaves in such a closely coordinated fashion that it has been called a "super-organism."

The evolving unit is not the individual, however, but a population of individuals. A species evolves through evolutionary changes in closely breeding groups, i.e., populations. An important factor involved is the separation of one population from another so that interbreeding becomes less likely. This separation can result from the appearance of geographic barriers of water or land. The initial phases of speciation may also involve reproductive isolation or separation because of physiological and behavioral differences.

There are numerous cases of related species in which perfectly viably hybrids can be produced, yet under natural conditions reproductive encounters between these forms rarely occur. Among the viviparous topminnows of the genus *Xiphophorus,* the platyfish, *X. maculatus,* and the swordtail, *X. helleri,* will hybridize in captive aquarium conditions. Some of these hybrids are fertile, and the breeders of tropical fishes have developed handsome strains from hybrid progenitors. The two species can be found living together in many Mexican and Central American rivers, and yet naturally occurring hybrids have never been found among the thousands of specimens collected. If placed in an aquarium where they can make a choice of mates, there is a high probability that mating will occur only among members of the same species. One reason for this selection appears to be behavioral. Although the courtship and mating patterns of the two species are practically identical, there are sufficient differences in the frequency of specific motor patterns so that hybridization becomes improbable under natural conditions. (See Fig. 48.)

The maintenance of a population is also based upon behavioral features. If undisturbed by man and other catastrophic environmental effects, the size of a population of animals remains remarkably stable. Darwin conceived of four major checks on the tendency of populations of organism to increase: availability of food, effects of predation, effects of climatic conditions, and the effects of disease. In addition to these, there is increasing evidence that there are behavioral and physiological controlling mechanisms that tend to stabilize a population, and that there is some sort of homeostasis and self-regulation in a population.

The ecologist V. C. Wynne-Edwards has pointed out that territoriality in many species determines the size and area occupied by the reproductive population. A territory is a defended area, and an individual without a territory, as in the case of many species of birds, may develop to maturity and be perfectly healthy, and yet be incapable of reproducing. Similarly, among gregarious and social animals, the order of social superiority will determine which individuals will reproduce and which will not. In spite of the tendency of so-called nature movies to show males fighting for dominance and for mates, the usual, normal encounters are not violent and often consist only of displays, roars, gestures, and other "threats." Tendencies among species for the formation of social or subsocial organizations such as herds, schools, and other groupings are actually advantageous for population control. In such groups, these "conventionalized" encounters are more likely to occur, and the reproductive population becomes limited through these encounters.

### Suggested Readings

Clark, E., L. R. Aronson, and M. Gordon. 1954. Mating behavior patterns in two sympatric species of xiphophorin fishes: their inheritance and significance in sexual isolation. *Bull. Amer. Mus. Nat. Hist.*, 103: 135–226.

DeVore, I. (ed.). 1965. *Primate Behavior.* Holt, Rinehart and Winston: New York.

Fraenkel, G. S., and D. C. Gunn. 1940. *The Orientation of Animals.* Reprinted edition, 1960. Dover Publications: New York.

Lehrman, D. S. 1953. A critique of Lorenz's "objectivistic" theory of animal behavior. *Quart. Rev. Biol.*, 28: 337–363.

Lehrman, D. S. 1964. The reproductive behavior of ring doves. *Scientific American*, 211: 48–54.

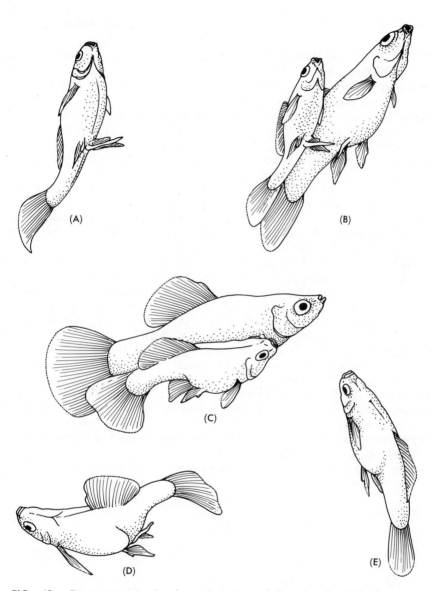

FIG. 48. Diagrammatic sketches of male and female platyfish illustrating various aspects of sexual behavior. (A) Male at the peak of gonopodial swing, ventral view. (B) Male platyfish (left) thrusting at a female, ventral view. (C) Male and female during copulation. The male is on the right side of the female. (D) Male showing S-curving behavior. (E) Male showing retiring behavior. (After E. Clark, L. R. Aronson, and M. Gordon, "Mating Behavior Patterns in Two Sympatric Species of Xiphophorin Fishes: Their Inheritance and Significance in Sexual Isolation," *Bull., Amer. Mus. Nat. Hist.*, vol. 103, 1954.)

Marler, P. R., and W. J. Hamilton. 1966. *Mechanisms of Animal Behavior*. John Wiley & Sons: New York.

Moltz, H. 1965. Contemporary instinct theory and the fixed action pattern. *Psychol. Rev.*, 72: 27–47.

Schneirla, T. C. 1956. The interrelationships of the "innate" and the "acquired" in instinctive behavior. *In L'Instinct dans le Comportement des Animaux et de l'Homme*. Masson: Paris. Pp. 387–452.

Schneirla, T. C. 1957. Theoretical considerations of cyclic processes in doryline ants. *Proc. Amer. Philos. Soc.*, 101: 106–133.

Schneirla, T. C. 1960. The army ants. *In Smithsonian Treasury of Science*. Simon and Schuster: New York. Pp. 664–696.

Schneirla, T. C.; and J. S. Rosenblatt. 1961. Behavorial organization and genesis of the social bond in insects and mammals. *Amer. J. Orthopsychiatry*, 31: 223–253.

Schaeffer, B., and D. E. Rosen. 1961. Major adaptive levels in the evolution of the actinopterygian feeding mechanism. *Amer. Zoologist*, 1: 187–204.

Shaw, E. 1962. The schooling of fishes. *Scientific American*, 206: 128–138.

Simpson, G. G. 1958. The study of evolution: methods and present status of theory. *In Behavior and Evolution* (A. Roe and G. G. Simpson, eds.), Yale University Press: New Haven. Pp. 7–26.

Tavolga, W. N. 1956. Visual, chemical, and sound stimuli as cues in the sex discriminatory behavior of gobiid fish, *Bathygobius soporator*. *Zoologica*, 41: 49–64.

Wecker, S. C. 1964. Habitat selection. *Scientific American*, 211: 109–116.

Wynne-Edwards, V. C. 1965. Self-regulating systems in populations of *American*, 211: 68–74.

Wynne-Edwards, V. C. 1965. Self-regulating systems in populations of animals. *Science*, 147: 1543–1548.

Wilson, E. O. 1965. Chemical communication in the social insects. *Science*, 149: 1064–1071.

# 7 EXPERIENCE
# AND THE DEVELOPMENT
# OF BEHAVIOR

In the previous sections, we have emphasized the central importance of studying animal behavior within the context of levels of organization. The concept of levels is developmental as well as evolutionary. Each species achieves a given level of organization that is effective enough in its echological niche for it to survive, but each individual of the species exists at many different levels at different stages of its development. At each stage, the individual has to be adapted to its particular environment. The environment and its requirements for survival for a caterpillar, a planktonic fish larva, and an embryo chick are quite different from the adaptations required of the adult forms of these animals. G. G. Simpson once stated that a population of organisms is not really a population of individuals, but, rather, a population of ontogenies.

To understand a behavior, therefore, it is necessary to investigate its development and to ask: How does it develop (descriptive analysis)? What are the factors that control its development (causal analysis)? In examining a particular behavior, it is not sufficient to begin when the behavior is first observable. What are the developmental antecedents? The problem becomes one of finding a starting point. The instant of hatching or birth is clearly an arbitrary point, and, often, one of practical convenience. How far back should one look? Does a fertilized egg exhibit behavior or behavioral antecedents? On some primitive level of organization it probably does. One could even say that DNA replication in mitosis is a form of behavior on a macromolecular level. If, however, we conceive of behavior as being an activity of a more or less integrated organism, a reasonable starting point would be at some embryonic stage at which the organism is developing an integrated morphology.

## BEHAVIORAL DEVELOPMENT IN THE CHICK

The chick is a convenient animal for many investigations, particularly embryological ones. After hatching, the animals are easily maintained under rigidly controlled conditions, and prior to hatching, the developing eggs are readily incubated in a simple apparatus. Many embryological studies have been done on this species by cutting windows in the egg shell, carrying out various micro-surgical procedures on the embryo, and then placing transparent glass or plastic over the window so that development can be observed. Similarly, the earliest movements of the embryo can be observed and, thus, the early development of behavior can be investigated.

In chickens, the eggs are fertilized internally. After the appropriate membranes and the shell are deposited in the mother's oviduct, the completed egg is laid, at which time about 12 to 16 hours of development have elapsed since fertilization. The total incubation time is about 21 days, and during this period the first muscular movements begin and develop to a peak of activity at hatching. The earliest movements are the contractions of the heart, beginning at about the thirtieth hour of development. These, at first, are quite irregular, but become more regular as the cardiac muscle develops further. Control from the nervous system contributes to this movement at a later time.

Movements of the skeletal muscles begin at just about the time skeletal muscle fibers differentiate. From about the fourth to the tenth day of development, slow twitching movements are frequent. At first, these involve the head and neck, partially aided by the rhythmic contractions of the huge, bulging heart. Gross movements of the trunk appear later. The limbs, after differentiating from simple buds, first move together with the trunk, but later begin to move separately. Eventually, movements of the tail, beak, and eyes can be observed. (See Fig. 49.)

The development of the nervous system coincides with the development of motility. The motor nerves differentiate first, and the sensory system becomes organized later, at which time the organism begins to respond to specific external stimuli.

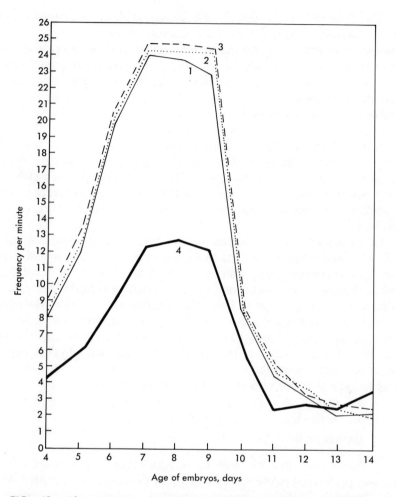

FIG. 49. The actions of chicken embryos during development: (1) swinging movements, (2) yolk sac movements, (3) amnion contractions, and (4) general body activities. (After P. Marler and W. J. Hamilton, *Mechanisms of Animal Behavior*, John Wiley & Sons, 1966.)

Many of these early embryonic movements have been called "spontaneous." This is a word often used to denote the fact that the cause of an event is not known. At the opposite extreme, some investigators believe that all these movements are responses to external stimuli. However, there are grounds for accepting the idea that at least some of these movements are endogenously evoked, in the sense that the process of growth and differentiation of neural tissue may itself act as a stimulus to muscle tissue.

The antecedents of coordinated behavior, such as pecking or walking, can be observed in the embryo. Head-bobbing, for example, is preceded by rhythmic contractions of the heart that thrust the head up and down. Proper positioning of the embryo in the egg with respect to gravity appears to be necessary for normal development of the legs and their muscles. Alternate leg movements begin by treading on the fluid-filled embryonic membranes. If the embryo is not correctly oriented, or if the yolk sac is shifted, normal locomotion does not develop.

It is evident that the appropriate embryonic environment is essential for the embryo to develop normally and for its behavior to organize properly. The antecedents of species-typical behavior develop in a rigidly controlled, species-typical environment. In the chick, the environment within the shell is maintained until the behavior is well on its way to being organized.

In its details, many problems on the behavioral development of the chick still need investigation. Some of the early observations and experiments should be replicated, and, in many cases, the causal relationships between the embryonic events and the post-hatching behavior are yet to be established. Correlation alone does not demonstrate a causal relationship. However, the principle upon which this work was done was a perfectly valid one: Species-typical behavior develops as a result of species-typical conditions. These conditions include the chemical and physical environment at all stages, from the interaction of DNA with the cytoplasm of the zygote to the effects of external stimuli on the individual.

### MATURATION

More than two hundred years ago, there was a belief that the adult was preformed in the embryo, and that development consisted simply of the "unfolding" of the characteristics of the individual. The recent discoveries in molecular genetics have led, unfortunately, to a revival of preformistic thinking. The genetic "code" is said to be "decoded" into the individual. Growth and differentiation, however, involve much more than this "unfolding" process. Genetic factors certainly influence growth and differentiation, but only in the particular context of the cellular environment at a particular stage. Certain mutant genes in the fruit fly (*Drosophila*), for example, are known to affect the structure of wings. This effect, however, is not directly upon wing growth, but, rather, on the response of the particular growth pattern to environmental temperature. The normal development of structure and behavior, therefore, are dependent upon the presence of normal environmental conditions, i.e., normal for the species.

Maturation, in this context, is defined as the organic basis of development, i.e., growth and differentiation guided by genetic and environmental and chemical factors that comprise the embryo, and, arise from the processes and results of growth and differentiation. These influences, in turn, affect the manner in which the genetic factors operate.

### EXPERIENCE

The stimulative effects that impinge upon the individual throughout its lifetime of development are called, collectively, *experience*. These stimulative effects include not only external stimuli mediated by specific sense organs, but also the wide range of chemical and physical changes that take place at all stages in the development of an individual. On the primitive, biochemical level, even the processes of maturation can function as part of the developmental experience of the individual.

Experience also has its *trace effects*. These are developmental effects of stimuli that are manifested at stages significantly later than those during which the stimuli were administered. In chick embryos, for example, conditioning to tactile stimuli before about ten days of incubation appears to have no effect at that time, yet these same embryos exhibit increased responsiveness at later stages. Exposure of the larvae of certain species of solitary wasps to the odor of a given species of prey organism has its trace effect in the adult. The adult wasp, in such cases, will deposit her eggs only on that prey species.

A well-studied example of trace effects is that of migrating salmon. These fish are spawned and hatched in fresh water streams, and they migrate downstream to the sea where they spend a major portion of their life. Upon attaining sexual maturity, the salmon migrate back to fresh water to spawn, but in doing so, individual animals return almost precisely to the streams where they were originally spawned. The sensory cues effective in the upstream migration are primarily chemical, and the fish are sensitive to extremely low concentrations of chemicals characteristic of their home streams. The stimulus and the response appear to be separated by a period of years, but the actual response to the stimulus may be the determination of a particular developmental pattern. This pattern eventually results in the development of the homing response.

The simplest kinds of experiential effects are on the chemical level of organization. Often such effects are controlled simply by the stimulus intensity, as in the case of an amoeba that approaches a dilute alkali and withdraws from a concentrated solution of the same chemical. Such responses are probably the result of cell membrane changes.

One investigator, many years ago, attempted to condition a response from the ciliate, *Paramecium*. By repeatedly forcing these protozoans to twist and turn their way through a maze made of capillary glass tubing, he found that their frequency and rate of turning was increased. It was later found that the process of "training" simply softened the pellicle, so that the animals became more flexible and could turn a corner more easily.

Taxes and kineses, as described earlier, are orienting responses closely controlled by the directional nature of the stimuli. The stimuli involved are a part of the developmental experience of the organism, and the stimuli themselves serve to guide the development of the organism toward a more efficient response.

Experience can modify behavior in a temporary, transitory way, as, for example, in effects on protozoan behavior by repeated stimulations. Although some investigators have called this primitive learning, the behavioral changes are temporary and after reverting to the initial physiological state, the organisms show no trace of effects of the prior experience.

Repeated stimulation of the hydroids or medusoids of coelenterates also produces a change in response that could be attributed to a change in the sensitivity of the receptors, i.e., *adaptation*. (This use of the word is not to be confused with adaptation in the evolutionary sense.) Unlike protozoa, the coelenterates possess a conducting system of nerve cells, but the level of modifiability of behavior is not very different. Here the nerve net does not act as a central controlling system, rather it is only a connecting system, and the organism is essentially bound in its responses to the capacities and properties of its receptors. Although the adaptation of coelenterate responses has been called learning by some investigators, the behavioral alterations are transitory and the organism is left essentially unchanged after these experiences.

Adaptation can also be demonstrated in higher organisms, including man. Exposure to strong light changes the distribution of pigment in the retina so that the eye becomes less sensitive to light, i.e., the familiar phenomenon of light adaptation. In some instances, as in skin touch receptors, the threshold of the sensory cells actually rises as a result of repeated stimulations.

Cessation of behavior, as a result of repeated stimulation, can actually result from a number of changes. One would be fatigue of the muscular system; another would be a change in the receptor system (adaptation). A third change leading to cessation of response is the result of some change in the integrative system. This last is usually termed *habituation*.

## LEARNING

A working definition of learning must include a long-lasting or permanent effect of experience upon behavior. The effect of an environmental experience is retained and incorporated in the development of behavior and in the performance of the organism. A central nervous system seems to be a prerequisite for learning to occur, and the most primitive manifestations of learning are to be found in such bilaterally symmetrical animals as flatworms and annelid worms.

The behavior of flatworms can be altered by the process of conditioning in which two kinds of stimuli are paired in time, as, for example, a light followed by an electric shock. In this instance, after 50 or 100 or more such paired stimuli, the animal will respond to the light alone by contractions or movements that normally would be stimulated by the shock. The performance of flatworms in a T-maze also indicates that conditioning can take place.

Among annelid worms, such as earthworms, the existence of conditioned responses can be demonstrated in T-mazes and a number of other situations. Here again, the conditioning is produced by pairing two stimuli and by repetition of the pairings. Given a choice of two directions, one leading toward a dark moist chamber and the other leading to an electric shock, the worm first learns to associate the sandpaper surface with the "wrong" alley and turns back before getting shocked. Eventually, it consistently takes the right turn into the dark chamber. Many trials are required to establish a significant change in the earthworm's behavior. (See Fig. 50).

A well-known method of conditioning behavior is often referred to as *classical* or *Pavlovian conditioning*. In his work with dogs, Pavlov paired the ringing of a bell with the subsequent presentation of food, and, after sufficient numbers of trials, the ringing of the bell alone was sufficient to stimulate the salivary flow associated normally with the presentation of food. The variants on this type of experiment are legion, but the essential feature is the invariable coupling of two disparate stimuli. The responses are often involuntary in nature, such as salivation or change in heart rate, and the response is usually retained for extremely long periods of time. Because the pairing of the stimuli in time is such an important requirement for this type of conditioning, many current workers refer to it as *contiguity learning*.

A more advanced type of learning is exhibited by higher invertebrates and most vertebrates. In a problem situation, the animal at first responds to the many stimuli in its environment in a variety of ways. With successive associations of related stimulus situations, the animal begins to narrow its

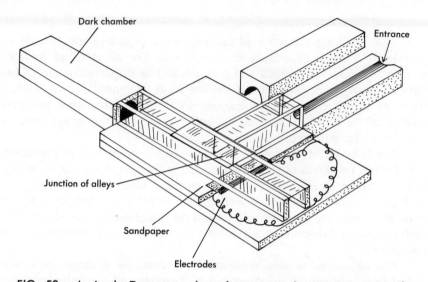

FIG. 50.  A simple T-maze used to demonstrate learning in an earthworm. *D*, dark chamber; *E*, electrodes; *J*, junction of alleys; *S*, sandpaper.
The alley walls are of plate glass; a removable piece of blotting paper
covers the floor. (After T. C. Schneirla, *Principles of Animal Psychology,*
Dover Publications, 1964.)

response repertoire in such a way that the most significant aspects of the
situations are responded to and other aspects are ignored. The probability
of pairing the appropriate stimuli and the appropriate response increases.
A rat in a problem box, maze, or other experimental situation initially
shows generalized responses, most of which are not appropriate to solving
the problem of attaining the food or escaping. After each time that success
is attained, the behavior of the animal becomes better organized and its
progress is more efficient. This is interpreted as essentially an expression of
Thorndike's Law of Effect in which associations are formed and strength-
ened by reward and reinforcement.

The process by which an insect learns a maze is especially instructive.
An ant in a maze with several T-choices and U-turns learns to find the
shortest route to the food box through a series of three stages. In stage 1,
there is a considerable amount of general activity and erratic behavior.
With repetition, the amount of variable behavior decreases, but the animal
shows no signs of improvement in avoiding blind alleys or taking short-
cuts. Stage 2 is characterized by a gradual shortening of runs into blind
alleys, and in stage 3, the blind alleys turns are completely eliminated and
the animal runs through the entire maze quickly and smoothly. The learn-

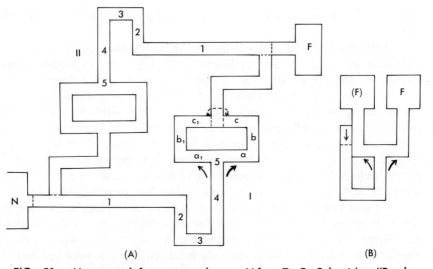

FIG. 51. Maze used for ants and rats. (After T. C. Schneirla, "Psycho-logical Comparison of Insect and Mammal," *Psychol. Beiträge,* vol. 6, 1962.)

(A) T-maze with U-alley approach to choice-point, in the pattern used for testing *Formica* ants.

I. The problem is presented in the direction N (Nest) to F (Foodbox). The subject's passage through approach alleys 2-4 generates a strong turning bias toward side $a$-$b$-$c$ and against side $a_1$-$b_1$-$c_1$. By blocking alley $c$ or alley $c_1$ at its end, alley $a_1$ or alley $a$ respectively is made the true-path turn at the choice-point.

II. Control situation with open alternatives at 5, through which the ant returns to N.

(B) T-maze with U-alley approach to choice-point as adapted by Witkin (1942) for rates. From the starting compartment (arrow) shown at left, the subject passes through a U-series of alleys which gives a strong turning bias toward the right turn (heavy arrow) at the choice-point. By placing food alternately in F and in (F) as each is learned, the experimenter forces the animal to shift its adjustment to the choice-point.

ing evidently takes place by a series of individual problem solutions at each choice point. (See Fig. 51.)

In similar mazes, rats learn the correct pathways with fewer errors and in fewer runs than do insects. Most significant, however, is the fact that the blind alley shortening occurs in abrupt jumps and no distinct stages can be detected. Subsequent alterations of the maze show that rats are capable of modifying their behavior readily in response to the new situations and of profiting from the experience of the initial learning. Ants, on the other hand, appear to learn a maze as a series of separate problems, and any changes have to be relearned as if they are completely new problems. (See Fig. 52.)

Although both the ant and the rat show learning, the process differs only quantitatively but also qualitatively. This is to be expected, because the rat and the ant are structurally and functionally very different animals.

A common question often asked of students of animal behavior is: "How intelligent is this animal?" This is really impossible to answer objectively, because we still have no adequate definition of intelligence, in spite of the fact that we intuitively seem to know something about it. Psychologists have yet to design an adequate, foolproof intelligence test even for human beings. The question posed above assumes that we know precisely what intelligence is and how to test it in a dog, fish, or planarian.

All that can be done, at the present time, is to place an animal in a situation where it must cope with some environmental problem. If one animal performs in what the experimenter considers the correct way, and another does not, does this necessarily mean anything beyond the fact that one animal behaved correctly while the other did not? If a dog cannot solve a problem involving the kind of manipulation that a monkey can do easily, does this mean that the monkey is smarter? Obviously, in interspecies comparisons, it is necessary to construct problems appropriate to the motor equipment of the species, but this is often impossible to accomplish and still retain the underlying equality of the problems. In addition, comparisons of this sort make the assumption that differences in intelligence, i.e., reasoning ability, are purely quantitative. Given equal problems, two different species might very well go about the solution differently. This is to be expected, because among other things, the two species have followed divergent developmental pathways and the perceptual world of one is not equivalent to the perceptual world of the other.

Problems on the psychological, physiological, neurological, and, indeed, biochemical basis of learning have occupied the attention of human and comparative psychologists for many years, and the reader is referred to the bibliography for a comprehensive coverage of this topic. In the context of a behavioral principle, it is clear that learning is a particular effect of stimulative experience. The experience has an effect on the development of behavior, i.e., a conditioned or learned response is formed. Moreover, Harlow has shown that the learning process itself may be an experience that can modify future learning. That is, animals have to "learn to learn." In this way, the stimulation that produces learning can have trace effects, just as experiences at other levels. It is important, therefore, to conceive of learning as a kind of integrative process that results from certain kinds of stimuli.

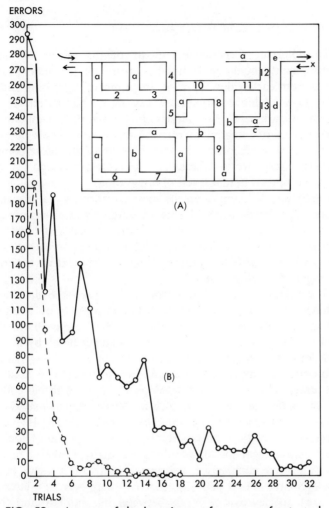

FIG. 52.   A curve of the learning performance of rats and ants in comparable mazes shows that rats will learn more rapidly. Additional observations, however, show that the two kinds of animals are qualitatively different in a way in which the learning takes place. (A) Maze used as learning test for rats and ants. (B) Solid line, ants; broken line, rats. (After T.C. Schneirla, "Psychological Comparison of Insect and Mammal," *Psychol. Beiträge*, vol. 6, 1962.)

## STIMULATIVE EFFECTS AT DIFFERENT LEVELS

To reiterate: *Experience* consists of the effects of stimulation upon development, including stimulation from all available sources and trace effects from earlier development. In primitive organisms and at early embryonic stages of higher organisms, experience has its effects on lower levels of organization. Higher levels of organization, including various kinds and degrees of integration, respond to different kinds of experience and in different ways. Learning is probably one of the most complex and highest levels of response to experience, and there are categories of learned behavior based upon different levels of integration.

Invertebrates, including even the most advanced social insects, have a rigidly controlled, species-typical kind of developmental experience. As a result, their behavior patterns tend to be stereotyped and highly resistant to alteration. Vertebrates, however, exhibit various levels of behavioral plasticity correlated with the greater range of stimulative experiences at different stages of development.

An instructive contrast can be drawn between the development of social behavior in a cat and a monkey. A kitten, when born, is a considerably more mature organism, structurally and physiologically, than a new-born monkey. The kitten's development has been regulated by its life in the rigid environment of the mother's uterus. When a kitten is reared in an artificial brooder, equipped with a mechanism for providing milk, warmth, and appropriate tactual stimuli, it develops into a cat with basically normal behavior. In some cases, however, such artificially reared cats do not care for their young as efficiently as normally raised animals. By contrast, a monkey reared in isolation shows virtually no development of social behavior and is virtually incapable of achieving a normal degree of reproductive behavior. A further comparison between an altricial (young born at an early developmental stage) and a precocial (young born at a later developmental stage) species can be made between the monkey and the chick. The incubation period within the egg provides the chick with a rigid, species-typical set of experiences, and the newly hatched animal has already developed its behavioral repertoire to a much greater extent than a new-born monkey.

The human species is probably the most altricial of all. To a new-born infant, the potentialities for a plastic behavioral development are tremendous, because the socialization process in human development is such a long one. It is here that our studies on behavioral development of lower animals can perhaps provide information on the problems of enhancing the potentialities of human behavioral development.

## MATURATION AND EXPERIENCE

The definitions of *maturation* as the processes of growth and differentiation and *experience* as the effects of stimulative processes are not exclusive. These two abstractions are not to be confused with any rigid dichotomies like nature vs. nurture or innate vs. acquired. The analyses of social behavior in the army ants and in the cat show that growth and differentiation have their stimulative trace effects, and experience is not confined to the stimuli from the external environment.

An excellent example of the inseparability and interdependence of maturation and experience can be seen in an analysis of the phenomenon of *imprinting*. Early in his investigations of animal behavior, K. Z. Lorenz observed this response. He found that the attention of newly hatched ducklings became fixed upon the first moving object of moderate size that they saw after hatching. The ducklings thereafter followed this object about as if it were their natural parent. The stimulus object in many observations was Lorenz himself. Many other species of birds have been found to become imprinted to follow a variety of objects, both natural and artificial. Imprinting appears to be a rapid type of learning and can occur only at early stages of behavioral development, at a time when the animal is experiencing its first encounters with the complex world outside the egg or the womb.

Numerous experimental studies have been reported on imprinting, primarily in birds, using models and abstract geometrical figures, varying in size, color, movement, etc. The results have shown that the requirements for an object to have imprinting value are broad and nonspecific. The important variables seem to be the size of the object, its intensity as a stimulus, and its rate of movement, and all experiments tend to emphasize the importance of moderate, low-intensity stimulation.

Within the egg, the bird embryo is normally subjected to only moderate, low-intensity stimulation. Chick embryos at late stages will respond to gentle tactual stimulation with forward movements of the head and, sometimes, turning toward the stimulus source. After the chick's eyes open, the head tends to turn so that stimulus objects become centered in the retina. Only low-intensity stimulation will evoke such *approach* responses. Approach responses are those that directly or indirectly tend to reduce the distance between the stimulus source and the individual. Strong stimuli tend to evoke *withdrawal* responses, e.g., turning away.

The above early approach behavior is a product of physiological and morphological maturation and the development of appropriate sensory-motor integration. The development of this behavior is guided, at all stages, by the environment of the egg and the stimulative effects of maturation itself.

The approach response appears to be self-reinforcing, because specific attributes of the stimulus object, such as details of shape, color, and coincident sounds, serve as conditioned stimuli. The animal, at this stage, is highly susceptible to conditioning, so that imprinting occurs rapidly. Under natural conditions, the newly hatched bird is most likely to see a moderate size, slowly moving, softly clucking mother hen. Imprinting, therefore, has considerable selective value for species survival.

At present, experimental evidence demonstrates only that the stimulus object in imprinting must be of low intensity, and the developmental basis for the response, as outlined above, is largely theoretical. It remains for further experimentation to test this theory, which states that imprinting is a form of early learning in which maturational processes play an important role in the initial generalized approach response toward low intensity stimulation. Central to this theory, as proposed by T. C. Schneirla, is the concept that maturation and experience form a fused system that guides the behavioral development of an individual through all its successive levels of organization.

## BIPHASIC BEHAVIOR

In an attempt to find an underlying basis for the development and evolution of behavior, T. C. Schneirla formulated a theory based upon the existence of primordial tendencies of organisms to move either toward or away from sources of stimulation. The main principle in this theory states that "intensity of stimulation basically determines the direction of the reaction." A weak stimulus results in an approach to the source, and a strong stimulus of the same kind produces a withdrawal response.

This biphasic, approach-withdrawal activity, universally distributed throughout the animal kingdom, can be demonstrated to exist in organisms from the amoeba to man. Animals at all levels of integration possess this biphasic behavior, although at the higher levels it is usually necessary to use embryonic or immature stages to demonstrate it.

Biphasic behavior can be observed in the forced responses of an amoeba toward weak light and away from strong light. A similar situation can be observed in the response of an earthworm to weak and strong illumination, and here the withdrawal response is apparently a function of the high-threshold, rapidly responding nerve fibers. At higher psychological levels, this biphasic behavior becomes modified and masked by the acquisition of behavioral modifications through the effects of experience. This is especially true of the higher vertebrates, yet even in the human species approach and withdrawal responses can be demonstrated. In a new-born infant, low-intensity acoustic and visual stimulations evoke facial reactions and extension movements that can be characterized as approach processes, whereas strong stimulations evoke vigorous grimaces, crying, turning-away, and other withdrawal responses. With further maturation and experience, the infant develops more specific responses such as smiling, reaching, and other integrated activities.

How does this theory apply to the development of behavior? If we accept the bulk of the data on the development of motility in the chick embryo, we can build up a plausible sequence of events. In the early stages, the environment within the egg is quite stable, and, because of the lack of much neural development, the development is steady, regular, and primarily concerned with the chemical, cellular, and tissue levels of organization. As organs form, their motor responsiveness to environmental stimuli appear, but because the environment is so regular, the responses, such as early heartbeat, are also regular. With the organization of nerve-muscle connections of somatic tissues, the early twitching movements begin. These are low-threshold systems, and their responses to low-intensity stimuli are sporadic. The contiguity in time between the environmental stimuli and the responses results in an increase in the frequency of the responses, probably as a result of sensitization and tissue differentiation. Such stimuli may be in part the developmental processes themselves, and, in part, external stimuli such as would originate from the mother hen's movements. The repetition of the stimulus-response events affects neural growth and differentiation, and, gradually, the responses become patterned into some regular sequence of muscle contractions.

At this point in time, any violent stimuli, such as the hen turning the egg or otherwise jostling it, tend to inhibit these early movement patterns. Both stimulation and inhibition soon are mediated by the earliest sensory systems of the embryo, mainly tactual and proprioceptive. The proprioceptors are those sensory systems that are particularly important in sending stimuli to the central nervous system concerning the state of muscle contraction and other internal systems. The proprioceptors, therefore, establish feedbacks of information so that efficient integration of the organism becomes possible. Only through some degree of stimulation can such feedbacks and, therefore, any integration develop.

As a result of development of integration, the early, low-threshold response systems eventually become organized into approach-type movements, such as head orientation, neck flexion, and bill opening. The movements that result from the inhibition of the approach responses also become integrated, but these are high-threshold systems and they develop later into withdrawal-type responses.

When a chick hatches, therefore, its approach systems are well developed, and respond readily to sources of low-intensity stimulation, such as small objects on the ground, slow moving objects, and low-intensity sounds. This change to a new environment necessitates the integration of new sensory systems, the visual and auditory.

This theory can be used to explain the process of imprinting, as well as the appearance of many other behavior patterns that seem to appear abruptly upon hatching, e.g., pecking and walking. The explanation does not require any assumptions of behavioral dichotomy of innate vs. acquired. We can also begin to understand the bases for phyletic differences in behavior.

By contrast with the chick, the infant human at birth comes into a new world with only the rudiments of a behavioral organization. Visual and auditory systems are virtually inoperative, and locomotion will take a considerable time to develop. This new world, however, is charged with new kinds of stimuli, many of which are high in intensity. The infant is exposed to these influences at an embryonic stage which is more plastic than the stage at which a chick is hatched, and the variability of the maturation-experience interactions will have a greater effect on behavioral development in a human infant than in a chick.

Although in its details, Schneirla's theory still requires considerable experimental substantiation, the basic ideas rest on fact that behavioral differences among animals result from

(a) Differences in level of organization attained at various stages.

(b) Differences in the patterns of maturation-experience systems that guide the individual's development at various stages.

All behavior patterns of all animals are to some degree modifiable and to some degree stereotyped. The question to ask is: What are the factors that guide the development and behavioral organization of an individual?

## Suggested Readings

Bitterman, M. E. 1964. The evolution of intelligence. *Scientific American*, 211: 92–100.

Hamburger, V. 1963. Some aspects of the embryology of behavior. *Quart. Rev. Biol.*, 38: 342–365.

Harnly, M. H. 1941. Flight capacity in relation to phenotypic and genotypic variations in the wings of *Drosophila melanogaster*. *J. Exp. Zool.*, 88: 263–274.

Harlow, H. F. 1949. The formation of learning sets. *Psychol. Rev.*, 56: 51–65.

Harlow, H. F., and M. K. Harlow. 1961. A study of animal affection. *Natural History*, 70: 48–55.

Harlow, H. F., and M. K. Harlow. 1962. Social deprivation in monkeys. *Scientific American,* 207: 137–146.

Hasler, A. D. 1960. Guideposts of migrating fishes. *Science,* 132: 785–792.

Kuo, Z. Y. 1932. Ontogeny of embryonic behavior in Aves. *J. Exp. Zool.,* 61: 395–430; 62: 453–487; *J. Comp. Psychol.,* 13: 245–271; 14: 109–121; *Psychol. Rev.,* 39: 499–515.

Maier, N. R. F., and T. C. Schmeirla. 1942. Mechanisms in conditioning. *Psychol. Rev.,* 49: 117–134.

Rosenblatt, J. S., and L. R. Aronson. 1958. The decline of sexual behavior in male cats after castration with special reference to the role of prior sexual experience. *Behaviour,* 12: 285–338.

Schneirla, T. C. 1962. Psychological comparison of insect and mammal. *Psychol. Beiträge,* 6: 509–520.

Schneirla, T. C. 1965. Aspects of stimulation and organization in approach/withdrawal processes underlying vertebrate behavioral development. *In Advances in the Study of Behavior* (D. S. Lehrman, R. A. Hinde and E. Shaw, eds.). Academic Press Inc.: New York. Pp. 1–74.

Schneirla, T. C. 1966. Behavioral development and comparative psychology. *Quart. Rev. Biol.,* 41: 283–302.

Sluckin, W. 1965. *Imprinting and Early Learning.* Aldine Publishing Co.: Chicago.

# BIBLIOGRAPHY

The following bibliography is reprinted in its entirety from *Bioscience,* February, 1967, pp. 125-132. Used by permission.

## ANIMAL BEHAVIOR

N. M. Jessop

*California Western University*
*San Diego*

This bibliography consists of a selection of books, monographs, and periodicals which are thought to represent important contributions to the scientific study of animal behavior. Each title has been assigned to one of several subsections on the basis of subjective judgment as to its major emphasis. (There are many borderline situations in which a title rightfully should be listed in more than one subsection, but such duplication was incompatible with holding the bibliography to manageable proportions.) A number of essentially narrative accounts have been included, which were deemed to be of particular merit in orienting the high school or lower division college student to the field of behavioral research; these titles are designated (L). Other titles are more suitable for study by advanced students. Books currently available in paper-back edition are designated (pa).

This bibliography by no means includes all books and monographs which have contributed to our understanding of animal behavior. The selection is oriented toward studies of unrestrained organisms living within the framework of their normal ecological relationships, but certain works have been included which concern the analysis of behavior under laboratory conditions. Titles dealing primarily with human behavior have not been included. Many purely descriptive accounts of animal behavior that do not seek to explain causation, development, or function of behavior have been omitted.

A number of works of considerable historic importance are now out of print, but some of these may become available through microfilm services or by reprinting. When a title is known to have been reprinted recently, both the original date of publication and the most recent date of reprinting have been indicated.

The compilation of this bibliography was carried out under the auspices of the Animal Behavior Society.

I.  BOOKS AND MONOGRAPHS

*A.  General*

Altman, J. 1966. *Organic Foundations of Animal Behavior.* Holt, Rinehart and Winston, New York.

Alverdes, F. 1932. *The Psychology of Animals in Relation to Human Psychology.* K. Paul, Trench, Trubner & Co., London.

Berlyne, D. E. 1960. *Conflict, Arousal and Curiosity.* McGraw-Hill Book Co., New York.

Bindra, D. 1959. *Motivation: A Systematic Reinterpretation.* Ronald Press Co., New York.

Birney, R. C., and R. C. Teevan (eds.). 1961. *Instinct.* D. Van Nostrand Co., Princeton, N.J. (pa)

Boulenger, E. G. 1931. *Animal Ways.* Ward, Lock & Co., Ltd., London. (L)

Broadhurst, P. L. 1963. *The Science of Animal Behaviour* Penguin Books, Baltimore, Md. (pa) (L)

Brown, J. S., et al. 1953. *Current Theory and Research in Motivation: A Symposium.* University of Nebraska Press, Lincoln.

Cloudsley-Thompson, J. 1960. *Animal Behaviour.* Oliver & Boyd, Edinburgh. (L)

Coghill, G. E. 1964. *Anatomy and the Problem of Behaviour.* Hafner Publishing Co., New York.

Davis, D. E. 1966. *Integral Animal Behavior.* Macmillan Co., New York. (pa) (L)

Dembowski, J. 1955. *Tierpsychologie.* Akademie-Verlag, Berlin.

Dethier, V. G., and E. Stellar. 1964. *Animal Behavior: Its Evolutionary and*

*Neurological Basis,* 2nd ed. Prentice-Hall, Englewood Cliffs, N.J. (pa) (L)

Eibl-Eibesfeldt, I. 1960. *Galápagos: The Noah's Ark of the Pacific.* Doubleday & Co., Garden City, N.Y. (L)

Goodwin, G. G., et al. 1961. *The Illustrated Encyclopedia of Animal Life: The Animal Kingdom: The Strange and Wonderful Ways of Mammals, Birds, Reptiles, Fishes and Insects: A New and Authentic Natural History of the Wildlife of the World.* Greystone Press, New York, (Hawthorn Books, Englewood Cliffs, N.J.) (L)

Gronefeld, G. 1965. *Understanding Animals.* William Heinemann, London. (L)

Hafez, E. S. E. (ed.). 1962. *The Behaviour of Domestic Animals.* Baillière, Tindall & Cox, London.

Hediger, H. 1955. *Studies of the Psychology and Behaviour of Captive Animals in Zoos and Circuses.* Butterworths, London.

Hediger, H. 1964 (1950). *Wild Animals in Captivity: An Outline of the Biology of Zoological Gardens.* Dover Publications, New York. (pa)

Hilgard, E. R., and D. G. Marquis. 1961. *Conditioning and Learning.* 2nd ed. rev. by G. A. Kimble. Appleton-Century-Crofts, New York.

Hinde, R. A. 1966. *Animal Behaviour: A Synthesis of Ethology and Comparative Psychology.* McGraw-Hill Book Co., New York.

Hingston, R. W. G. 1929. *Instinct and Intelligence.* Macmillan Co., New York.

Holmes, R. J. 1916. *Studies in Animal Behavior.* R. G. Badger, Boston, Mass.

Hull, C. L. 1952. *A Behavior System: An Introduction to Behavior Theory Concerning the Individual Organism.* Yale University Press, New Haven, Conn.

Katz, R. 1949 (1937). *Animals and Men: Studies in Comparative Psychology.* Penguin Books, Baltimore, Md. (pa) (L)

Koch, S. 1962. *Psychology: A Study of a Science. Study II: Empirical Substructure and Relations with Other Sciences.* v. 4, Biologically Oriented Fields: Their Place in Psychology and in Biological Science. McGraw-Hill Book Co., New York.

Lehrman, D. S., R. Hinde, and E. Shaw (eds.). 1965. *Advances in the Study of Behavior,* v. 1. Academic Press, Inc., New York.

Logan, F. A. 1960. *Incentive: How the Conditions of Reinforcement Affect the Performance of Rats.* Yale University Press, New Haven, Conn.

Lorenz, K. Z. 1952. *King Solomon's Ring.* Thomas Y. Crowell Co., New York. (pa) (L)

Maier, N. R. F., and T. C. Schneirla. 1964. *Principles of Animal Psychology,* enlarged ed. Dover Publications, New York.

Marler, P., and W. J. Hamilton, Ill. 1966. *Mechanisms of Animal Behavior.* John Wiley & Sons, New York.

McGill, T. E. (ed.). 1965. *Readings in Animal Behavior.* Holt, Rinehart and Winston, New York.

Morgan, C. L. 1930. *The Animal Mind.* Longmans, Green & Co., New York.

Noble, R. C. 1945. *The Nature of the Beast: A Popular Account of Animal*

*Psychology from the Point of View of a Naturalist.* (G. K. Noble.) Doubleday & Co., Garden City, N.Y. (L)

Osgood, C. E. 1953. *Method and Theory in Experimental Psychology.* Oxford University Press, New York.

Pfeiffer, C. C., and J. R. Smythies (eds.). 1959—. *International Review of Neurobiology,* v. 1—. Academic Press, Inc., New York.

Pickwell, G. B. 1940. *Animals in Action.* McGraw-Hill Book Co., New York. (L)

Ratner, S. C., and M. R. Denny. 1964. *Comparative Psychology: Research in Animal Behavior.* Dorsey Press, Homewood, Ill.

Ritter, W. E. 1928. *Animal and Human Conduct.* G. Allen & Unwin, London.

Romanes, G. J. 1882. *Animal Intelligence.* The Intern. Sci. Ser., no. 41, London.

Russell, E. S. 1934. *The Behaviour of Animals: An Introduction to Its Study.* E. Arnold & Co., London.

Sanderson, I. T. 1937. *Animal Treasure.* Viking Press, New York. (L)

Schiller, C. H. (ed. & trans.). 1957. *Instinctive Behavior: The Development of a Modern Concept.* International Universities Press, New York.

Scientific American. 1955. *Twentieth-century Bestiary.* Simon and Schuster, New York. (pa) (L)

Scott, J. P. 1963 (1958). *Animal Behavior.* Doubleday & Co., Garden City, N.Y. (pa) (L)

Skinner, B. F. 1938. *The Behavior of Organisms: An Experimental Analysis.* Appleton-Century-Crofts, New York.

Smythe, R. H. 1962. *Animal Habits: The Things Animals Do.* Charles C Thomas, Springfield, Ill. (L)

Sokolov, Y. (E.) N. 1963. *Perception and the Conditioned Reflex.* Pergamon Press, New York.

Stevens, S. S. (ed.). 1951. *Handbook of Experimental Psychology.* John Wiley & Sons, New York.

Stone, C. P. (ed.). 1950—. *Annual Review of Psychology,* v. 1—. Annual Reviews, Inc., Palo Alto, Calif.

Stone, C. P. (ed.). 1951. *Comparative Psychology,* 3rd ed. Prentice-Hall, Englewood Cliffs, N.J.

Tembrock, G. 1964. *Verhaltensforschung: Eine Einfuhrung in die Tier-Ethologie.* Gustav Fischer-Verlag, Jena.

Thorndike, E. L. 1965 (1911). *Animal Intelligence: Experimental Studies.* Hafner Publishing Co., New York.

Thorpe, W. H. 1963. *Learning and Instinct in Animals,* 2nd ed. Harvard University Press, Cambridge, Mass.

Thorpe, W. H., and O. L. Zangwill (eds.). 1961. *Current Problems in Animal Behaviour.* Cambridge University Press, Cambridge.

Tinbergen, N. 1951. *A Study of Instinct.* Clarendon Press, Oxford.

Tinbergen, N. 1958. *Curious Naturalists.* Country Life, London. (L)

Tinbergen, N. 1965. *Animal Behavior.* Time-Life Books, Chicago, Ill. (L)

Tolman, E. C. 1932. *Purposive Behavior in Animals and Men.* The Century Psychology Series.

Verplanck, W. S. 1957. *A Glossary of Some Terms Used in the Objective Science of Behavior.* American Psychological Association, Washington, D.C.

Warden, C. J., T. N. Jenkins, and L. H. Warner. 1935-40. *Comparative Psychology: A Comprehensive Treatise.* 3 vols. Ronald Press Co., New York.

Waters, R. H., D. A. Rethlingshafer, and W. E. Caldwell (eds.). 1960. *Principles of Comparative Psychology.* McGraw-Hill Book Co., New York.

Watson, J. B. 1914. *Behavior: An Introduction to Comparative Psychology.* Holt, Rinehart and Winston, New York.

Young, J. Z. 1962. *The Life of Vertebrates,* 2nd ed. Clarendon Press, Oxford.

Young, P. T. 1961. *Motivation and Emotion: A Survey of the Determinants of Human and Animal Activity.* John Wiley & Sons, New York.


B.  *Studies of specific animal groups*
    (*See also listings in other categories*)

     1.  Invertebrates

Burr, M. 1954. *The Insect Legion,* 2nd ed. J. Nisbet & Co., London. (L)

Carthy, J. D. 1962 (1958). *An Introduction to the Behaviour of Invertebrates.* Hafner Publishing Co., New York.

Carthy, J. D. 1965. *The Behaviour of Anthropods.* W. H. Freeman & Co., San Francisco. (pa) (L)

Cloudsley-Thompson, J. L. 1958. *Spiders, Scorpions and Mites: The Ecology and Natural History of Woodlice, Myriapods and Arachnids.* Pergamon Press, New York.

Dethier, V. G. 1962. *To Know a Fly.* Holden-Day, San Francisco. (L)

Emerton, J. H. 1962 (1902). *The Common Spiders of the United States.* Dover Publications, New York.

Evans, H. E. 1963. *Wasp Farm.* The Natural History Press (Doubleday & Co.), Garden City, N.Y. (L)

Evans, H. E. 1966. *The Comparative Ethology and Evolution of the Sand Wasps.* Harvard University Press, Cambridge, Mass.

Gertsch, W. J. 1949. *American Spiders.* D. Van Nostrand Co., Princeton, N.J.

Jennings, H. S. 1962. *Behavior of the Lower Organisms,* 2nd ed. Indiana University Press, Bloomington, Ind.

Savory, T. H. 1959. *Instinctive Living: A Study of Invertebrate Behaviour.* Pergamon Press, New York.

Thorpe, W. H., and D. Davenport (eds.). 1965. *Learning and Associated Phenomena in Invertebrates.* Bailliére, Tindall & Cox, London.

Waterman, T. H. (ed.). 1961. *Physiology of Crustacea.* v. 2, *Sense Organs, Integration and Behavior.* Academic Press, Inc., New York.

Wells, M. J. 1962. *Brain and Behavior in Cephalopods.* Stanford University Press, Stanford, Calif.

Wichterman, R. 1953. *The Biology of Paramecium.* Blakiston Co., New York (McGraw-Hill Book Co.).


     2.  Fishes

Baerends, G. P., and J. M. Baerends-Van Roon. 1950. *An Introduction to the*

*Study of the Ethology of Cichlid Fishes.* Behaviour, Supplement no. 1. E. J. Brill, Leiden.

Brown, M. E. (ed.). 1961. *The Physiology of Fishes.* v. 2, *Behavior.* Academic Press, Inc., New York.

Gilbert, P. W. (ed.). 1963. *Sharks and Survival.* D. C. Heath & Co., Boston, Mass. (L)

Schultz, L. P., and E. M. Stern. 1948. *The Ways of Fishes.* D. Van Nostrand Co., Princeton, N.J. (L)

Liley, N. R. 1966. *Ethological Isolating Mechanisms in Four Species of Poeciliid Fishes.* Behaviour, Supplement no. 13. E. J. Brill, Leiden.

Van Den Nieuwenhuizen, A. 1964. *Tropical Aquarium Fish: Their Habits and Breeding Behaviour.* D. Van Nostrand Co., Princeton, N.J. (L)

### 3. Herptiles

Bellairs, A. d'a. 1960. *Reptiles: Life History, Evolution and Structure.* Harper & Row, Publishers, New York. (pa) (L)

Ditmars, R. L. 1939. *Thrills of a Naturalist's Quest.* Macmillan Co., New York. (L)

Oliver, J. A. 1955. *The Nautral History of North American Amphibians and Reptiles.* D. Van Nostrand Co., Princeton, N.J.

### 4. Birds

Armstrong, E. A. 1965 (1942). *Bird Display and Behaviour: An Introduction to the Study of Bird Psychology.* Dover Publications, New York. (pa)

Fisher, J. 1952. *The Fulmar.* John de Graff, Tuckahoe, N.Y. (L)

Fisher, J., and R. M. Lockley. 1954. *Sea-birds: An Introduction to the Natural History of the Sea-birds of the North Atlantic.* Collins, Sons & Co., London. (L)

Glasier, P. 1963. *As the Falcon Her Bells.* E. P. Dutton & Co. New York. (L)

Hinde, R. A. 1952. *The Behaviour of the Great Tit* (Parus major) *and Some Other Related Species.* Behaviour, Supplement no. 2, E. J. Brill, Leiden.

Hochbaum, H. A. 1959. (1944). *The Canvasback on a Prairie Marsh.* Stackpole Co., Harrisburg, Pa. (L)

Howard, H. E. 1929. *An Introduction to the Study of Bird Behaviour.* Cambridge University Press, Cambridge.

Howard, H. E. 1940. *A Waterhen's World.* Cambridge University Press, New York. (L)

Johnsgard, P. A. 1965. *Handbook of Waterfowl Behavior.* Comstock Publishing Associates, Ithaca, N.Y.

Kirkman, F. B. 1937. *Bird Behaviour: A Contribution Based Chiefly on a Study of the Black-Headed Gull.* Nelson, London.

Lack, D. 1943. *The Life of the Robin.* Penguin Books, London. (L)

Latham, R. M. 1956. *Complete Book of the Wild Turkey.* Stackpole Co., Harrisburg, Pa.

Lister, M. 1962. *A Bird and Its Bush.* Phoenix House, London (L)

Lockley, R. M. 1961. *Shearwaters.* Doubleday & Co., Garden City, N.Y. (pa) (L)

Lockley, R. M. 1962. *Puffins.* Doubleday & Co., Garden City, N.Y. (pa) (L)

Marler, P. 1956. *Behaviour of the Chaffinch* Fringilla Coelebs. Behaviour, Supplement no. 5. E. J. Brill, Leiden.

Marshall, A. J. (ed.). 1961. *Biology and Comparative Physiology of Birds.* 2 vols. Academic Press, Inc., New York.

Nice, M. M. 1964 (1937) (1943). *Studies in the Life History of the Song Sparrow.* 2 vols. Dover Publications, New York. (pa)

Tinbergen, N. 1961 (1953). *The Herring Gull's World.* Basic Books, New York. (L)

Van Tets, G. F. 1965. *A Comparative Study of Some Social Communication Patterns in the Pelecaniformes.* American Ornithologists Union.

Wing, L. W. 1956. *Natural History of Birds.* Ronald Press Co., New York. (L)

5. Mammals

Adamson, J. 1960. *Born Free: A Lioness of Two Worlds.* Collins & Harvill Press, London. (pa) (L)

Adamson, J. 1961. *Living Free: The Story of Elsa and Her Cubs.* Collins & Harvill Press, London. (L)

Barnett, S. A. 1963. (*The Rat.*) *A Study on Behaviour: Principles of Ethology and Behavioural Physiology, Displayed Mainly in the Rat.* Methuen & Co., London.

Boulière, F. 1956. *The Natural History of Mammals,* 2nd ed. Alfred A. Knopf, New York. (L)

Buechner, H. K. 1960. *The Bighorn Sheep in the United States.* Wildlife Monographs, no. 4. The Wildlife Society, Washington, D.C.

Carpenter, C. R. 1965. *Naturalistic Behavior of Non-human Primates.* Pennsylvania University Press, University Park.

Crisler, L. 1958. *Arctic Wild.* Harper & Row, Publishers, New York. (L)

DeVore, I. (ed.). 1965. *Primate Behavior: Field Studies of Monkeys and Apes.* Holt, Rinehart and Winston, New York.

Eisenberg, J. F. 1963. The Behavior of Heteromyid Rodents. *Univ. Calif. Publ. in Zool.,* no. 69 University of California Press, Berkeley.

Farris, E. J., and J. Q. Griffith (eds.). 1949. *The Rat in Laboratory Investigation,* 2nd ed. J. B. Lippincott Co., Philadelphia.

Fox, M. W. 1965. *Canine Behavior.* Charles C Thomas, Springfield, Ill.

Guthrie, E. R., and G. P. Horton. 1946. *Cats in a Puzzle Box.* Holt, Rinehart and Winston, New York.

Hooton, E. A. 1940. *Why Men Behave Like Apes, and Vice Versa: or, Body and Behavior* (Vanuxem Lectures). Oxford University Press, London.

Hurrell, H. G. 1963. *Atlanta My Seal.* William Kimber, London. (L)

Klüver, H. 1961 (1933). *Behavior Mechanisms in Monkeys.* University of Chicago Press, Chicago, Ill. (pa)

Kroot, P. 1963. *Bears in the Family.* Oliver and Boyd, London. (L)

Maxwell, G. 1960. *Ring of Bright Water.* E. P. Dutton & Co., London. (L)

McCabe, T. T., and B. D. Blanchard. 1950. *Three Species of Peromyscus.* Rood Associates, Santa Barbara, Calif.

Mech, L. D. 1966. *The Wolves of Isle Royale*. Fauna of National Parks of United States, Fauna series no. 7. Superintendent of Documents, Washington, D.C.

Mellen, I. M. 1952. *The Natural History of the Pig*. Exposition Press, New York.

Moynihan, M. 1964. Some Behavior Patterns of Playtyrrhine Monkeys. 1. The Night Monkey (*Actus trivirgatus*). *Smithsonian Misc. Collections*, v. 146, no. 5. Smithsonian Institution, Washington, D.C.

Munn, N. 1950. *Handbook of Psychological Research on the Rat: An Introduction to Animal Psychology*. Houghton Mifflin Co., Boston, Mass.

Murie, A. 1940. *Ecology of the Coyote in the Yellowstone:* Fauna of National Parks of United States, Fauna series no. 4. Superintendent of Documents, Washington, D.C.

Murie, A. 1944. *The Wolves of Mt. McKinley*. Fauna of National Parks of United States, Fauna series no. 5. Superintendent of Documents, Washington, D.C.

Schaller, G. B. 1963. *The Mountain Gorilla: Ecology and Behavior*. University of Chicago Press, Chicago, Ill.

Schaller, G. B. 1964. *The Year of the Gorilla*. Ballantine Books, New York. (pa) (L)

Schrier, A. M., H. F. Harlow, and F. Stollnitz (eds.). 1965. *Behavior of Nonhuman Primates: Modern Research Trends,* vols. 1 and 2. Academic Press, Inc., New York.

Seton, E. T. 1923. *Wild Animals at Home*. Doubleday & Co., Garden City, N.Y. (L)

Seton, E. T. 1953 (1929). *Lives of Game Animals*. Charles T. Branford Co., Newton Centre, Mass. (L)

Snell, G. D. (ed.). 1956. *The Biology of the Laboratory Mouse*. Dover Publications, New York.

Walker, E. P., et al. 1964. *Mammals of the World,* vols. 1-3. Johns Hopkins Press, Baltimore, Md.

Williams, M. 1956. *Horse Psychology*. Methuen & Co., London.

Wilson, C., and E. Weston. 1947. *The Cats of Wildcat Hill*. Duell, Sloan & Pearce, New York. (Meredith Press).

Yerkes, R. M. 1943, *Chimpanzees: A Laboratory Colony*. Yale University Press, New Haven, Conn.

Young, J. Z. 1957. *The Life of Mammals*. Oxford University Press, New York.

Zoological Society of London. 1962. *The Primates*. Symposia no. 10 Academic Press, Inc., New York.

## C.   Social behavior and ecology

Allee, W. C. 1931. *Animal Aggregations: A Study in General Sociology*. University of Chicago Press, Chicago, Ill.

Allee, W. C. 1958. *The Social Life of Animals*. Rev. ed. Beacon Press, Inc., Boston, Mass. (pa) (L)

Allee, W. C., O. Park, A. E. Emerson, T. Park, and K. P. Schmidt. 1965 (1949). *Principles of Animal Ecology.* W. B. Saunders Co., Philadelphia, Pa.

Alverdes, F. 1927. *Social Life in the Animal World.* Harcourt, Brace & World, New York.

Andrewartha, H. G. 1963. *Introduction to the Study of Animal Populations.* University of Chicago Press, Chicago, Ill. (pa) (L)

Andrewartha, H. G., and L. C. Birch. 1961 (1954). *The Distribution and Abundance of Animals.* University of Chicago Press, Chicago, Ill.

Biological Symposia. 1942. *Levels of Integration in Biological and Social Systems,* no. 8. Jacques Cattell Press, Lancaster, Pa.

Brown, J. 1964. The Integration of Agonistic Behavior in the Steller's Jay *Cyanocitta stelleri* (Gmelin). *Univ. Calif. Publ. Zool.,* Berkeley, v. 60, No. 4, pp. 223-328.

Buddenbrock, W. Von. 1956. *The Love-life of Animals.* F. Muller, London.

Calhoun, J. B. 1963. The Ecology and Sociology of the Norway Rat. *U.S. Public Health Service Publ.* no. 1008. U.S. Government Printing Office, Washington, D.C.

Carpenter, C. R. 1934. *A Field Study of the Behavior and Social Relations of Howling Monkeys.* Comparative Psych. Monographs no. 10. Johns Hopkins University Press, Baltimore, Md.

Carthy, J. D., and F. J. Ebling (eds.). 1964. *The Natural History of Aggression.* Academic Press, Inc., New York.

Carthy, J. D., 1957. *Population Studies: Animal Ecology and Demography.* Cold Spring Harbor Symp. Quant. Biol. v. 22.

Conference on Group Processes. 1954. *Group Processes, Transactions.* Josiah Macey Jr. Foundation, New York.

Darling, F. F. 1938. *Bird Flocks and the Breeding Cycle: A Contribution to the Study of Avian Sociology.* Cambridge University Press, Cambridge.

Darling, F. F. 1964 (1937). *A Herd of Red Deer: A Study in Animal Behavior.* Doubleday & Co., New York. (pa) (L)

Dice, L. R. 1952. *Natural Communities.* University of Michigan Press, Ann Arbor.

Etkin, W. (ed.). 1964. *Social Behavior and Organization Among Vertebrates.* University of Chicago Press, Chicago, Ill.

Ford, C. S., and F. A. Beach. 1951. *Patterns of Sexual Behavior.* Harper & Row, Publishers, New York.

Friedmann, H. 1960. The Parasitic Weaverbirds, *U.S. National Museum Bull.* 223. Smithsonian Institution, Washington, D.C.

Friedmann, H. 1963. Host Relations of the Parasitic Cowbirds. *U.S. National Museum Bull.* 233. Smithsonian Institution, Washington, D.C.

Grasse, P. P. (ed.). 1952. *Structure et Physiologie des Societes Animales.* Colloques Internationaux, no. 34. Centre National de la Recherche Scientifique, Paris.

Hesse, R., W. C. Allee, and K. P. Schmidt. 1951. *Ecological Animal Geography.* 2nd ed. John Wiley & Sons, New York.

Houlihan, R T. 1964. The Relationship of Population Density to Endocrine and Metabolic Changes in the California Vole, *Microtus calfornicus*. *Univ. Calif. Publ. Zool.*, Berkeley, v. 65, no. 5.

Howard, E. 1948 (1920). *Territory in Bird Life*. Collins, Sons & Co., London.

Kaufmann, J. H. 1962. *Ecology and Social Behavior of the Coati Nasua narica on Barro Colorado Island, Panama*. University of California Press, Berkeley.

King, J. A. 1955. Social Behavior, Social Organization, and Population Dynamics in a Black-tailed Prairiedog Town in the Black Hills of South Dakota. *Contrib. Lab. Vertebrate Biol.* no. 67. University of Michigan Press, Ann Arbor.

Klopfer, P. H. 1962. *Behavioral Aspects of Ecology*. Prentice-Hall, Englewood Cliffs, N.J. (L)

Kruuk, H. 1964. *Predators and Anti-predator Behaviour of the Black-headed Gull* (Larus ridibundus L.). Behaviour, Supplement no. 11. E. J. Brill, Leiden.

Leiderman, P. H., and D. Shapiro, (eds.). 1964. *Psychobiological Approaches to Social Behavior*. Stanford University Press, Stanford, Calif.

Lorenz, K. Z. 1966. *On Aggression*. Harcourt, Brace & World, New York. (L)

MacMillen, R. E. 1964. Population Ecology, Water Relations and Social Behavior of a Southern California Semidesert Rodent Fauna. *Univ. Calif. Publ. Zool.*, Berkeley, v. 71.

McKinney, F. 1961. *An Analysis of the Displays of the European Eider* (Somateria mollissima mollissima) *and the Pacific Eider* (Somateria mollissima V. Nigra) *Bonaparte*. Behaviour, Supplement no. 7. E. J. Brill, Leiden.

Meade, J. E., and A. S. Parkes. (eds.). 1965. *Biological Aspects of Social Problems: A Symposium Held by the Eugenics Society in October 1964*. Plenum Press, New York.

Meyerriecks, A. J. 1960. *Comparative Breeding Behavior of Four Species of North American Herons*. Nuttall Ornithological Club, Cambridge, Mass.

Michener, C. D., and M. H. Michener. 1951. *American Social Insects*. D. Van Nostrand Co., Princeton, N.J. (L)

Milne, L. J., and M. J. Milne. 1950. *The Mating Instinct*. Little, Brown & Co., Boston, Mass. (L)

Morris, D. 1958. *The Reproductive Behaviour of the Ten-spined Stickleback* (Pygoteus pungitius L.) Behaviour, Supplement no. 6. E. J. Brill, Leiden.

Moynihan, M. 1955. *Some Aspects of Reproductive Behaviour in the Black-headed Gull* (Larus ridibundus ridibundus L.). Behaviour, Supplement no. 4. E. J. Brill, Leiden.

Moynihan, M. 1962. *Hostile and Sexual Behaviour Patterns of South American and Pacific Laridae*. Behaviour, Supplement no. 8. E. J. Brill, Leiden.

Portmann, A. 1964. *Animals As Social Beings*. Harper & Row, Publishers, New York. (pa) (L)

Rheingold, H. L. (ed.). 1963. *Maternal Behavior in Mammals*. John Wiley & Sons, New York.

Ribbands, R. 1964 (1953). *The Behavior and Social Life of Honeybees.* Dover Publications, New York (pa) (L)

Richards, O. W. 1961 (1953). *The Social Insects.* Harper & Row, Publishers, New York.

Scott, J. P. 1958. *Aggression.* University of Chicago Press, Chicago, Ill.

Society for Experimental Biology. 1961. *Mechanisms in Biological Competition.* Symposia no. 15. Cambridge University Press, New York.

Southwick, C. H. (ed.). 1963. *Primate Social Behavior.* D. Van Nostrand Co., Princeton, N.J. (pa)

Stonor, C. R. 1940. *Courtship and Display Among Birds.* Country Life, London (L)

Tinbergen, N. 1953. *Social Behaviour in Animals: With Special Reference to Vertebrates.* John Wiley & Sons, New York. (L)

Van Iersel, J. J. A. 1953. *An Analysis of the Parental Behaviour of the Male Three-spined Stickleback* (Gasterosteus aculeatus). Behaviour, Supplement no. 3. E. J. Brill, Leiden.

Wheeler, W. M. 1923. *Social Life Among the Insects.* Harcourt, Brace & World, New York.

Wheeler, W. M. 1928. *The Social Insects: Their Origin and Evolution.* International Library of Psychology, Philosophy & Scientific Method, London.

Wynne-Edwards, V. C. 1962. *Animal Dispersion in Relation to Social Behaviour.* Oliver & Boyd, Edinburgh.

Zoological Society of London. 1965. *Social Organization of Animal Communities.* Symposia no. 14. Academic Press, Inc., New York. (pa)

### D.   Communication, including bioacoustics

Armstrong, E. A. 1963. *A Study of Bird Song.* Oxford University Press, New York.

Busnel, R. G. (ed.). 1963. *Acoustic Behaviour of Animals.* American Elsevier Publishing Co., New York.

Capranica, R. R. 1965. *The Evoked Vocal Response of the Bullfrog: A Study of Communication by Sound.* The M.I.T. Press, Cambridge, Mass.

Collias, N. E. 1964. *Animal Language.* (BSCS Pamphlet.) D. C. Heath & Co., Boston, Mass. (pa) (L)

Darwin, C. R. 1965 (1899). *The Expression of the Emotions in Man and Animals.* University of Chicago Press, Chicago, Ill. (pa)

Frings, H., and M. Frings. 1964. *Animal Communication.* Blaisdell Publishing Co., Waltham, Mass. (L)

Frings, M., and H. Frings. 1960. *Sound Production and Sound Reception by Insects: A Bibliography.* Pennsylvania State University Press, University Park.

Frisch, K. von. 1954. *The Dancing Bees.* Methuen & Co., London.

Frisch, K. von. 1965. *Tanzsprache und Orientierung der Bienen.* Springer-Verlag, Berlin.

Haskell, P. T. 1961. *Insect Sounds.* Quadrangle Books, Chicago, Ill. (L)

Huxley, J., and L. Koch. 1964. *Animal Language* (with phonodisc). Grosset & Dunlap, New York. (L)

Jacobson, M. 1965. *Insect Sex Attractants.* Interscience Publishers, New York. (John Wiley & Sons, Inc.)

Lanyon, W. E., and W. N. Tavolga (eds.). 1960. *Animal Sounds and Communication* (with phonodisc). Proc. Symp., Indiana University, 1958. AIBS, Washington, D.C.

Lindauer, M. 1961. *Communication Among Social Bees.* Harvard University Press, Cambridge, Mass.

Pierce, G. W. 1948. *The Songs of Insects: With Related Material on the Production, Propagation, Detection and Measurement of Sonic and Supersonic Vibrations.* Harvard University Press, Cambridge, Mass.

Rosenblith, W. A. (ed.). 1964. *Symposium on Principles of Sensory Communication, Endicott House, 1959.* The M.I.T. Press, Cambridge, Mass.

Thorpe, W. H. 1961. *Bird Song: The Biology of Vocal Communication and Expression in Birds.* Cambridge University Press, Cambridge.

Zoological Society of London. 1962. *Biological Acoustics.* Symposia no. 7. Academic Press, Inc., New York. (pa)

### E. Orientation, navigation, and migration

Carr, A. 1962. *Guideposts of Animal Navigation.* (BSCS pamphlet.) D. C. Heath & Co., Boston, Mass. (pa) (L)

Carthy, J. D. 1963 (1956). *Animal Navigation: How Animals Find Their Way About.* G. Allen & Unwin, London. (L)

Dorst, J. 1962. *The Migrations of Birds.* Houghton Mifflin Co., Boston, Mass. (L)

Fraenkel, G. S., and D. L. Gunn. 1940. *The Orientation of Animals: Kineses, Taxes and Compass Reactions.* Dover Publications, New York. (pa)

Griffin, D. R. 1958. *Listening in the Dark: The Acoustic Orientation of Bats and Men.* Yale University Press, New Haven, Conn. (L)

Griffin, D. R. 1959. *Echoes of Bats and Men.* Doubleday & Co., Garden City, N.Y. (pa) (L)

Griffin, D. R. 1964. *Bird Migration: The Biology and Physics of Orientation Behavior.* Doubleday & Co., Garden City, N.Y. (pa) (L)

Groot, C. 1965. *On the Orientation of Young Sockeye Salmon* (Oncorhynchus nerka) *During Their Seaward Migration Out of Lakes.* Behaviour, Supplement no. 14. E. J. Brill, Leiden.

Hasler, A. D. 1966. *Underwater Guideposts: Homing of Salmon.* The University of Wisconsin Press, Madison.

Hochbaum, H. A. 1956. *Travels and Traditions of Waterfowl.* University of Minnesota Press, Minneapolis. (L)

Jameson, W. 1961. *The Wandering Albatross.* Doubleday & Co., Garden City, N.Y. (L)

Loeb, J. 1918. *Forced Movements, Tropisms and Animal Conduct.* J. B. Lippincott Co., Philadelphia, Pa.

Matthews, G. V. T. 1955. *Bird Navigation*. Cambridge University Press, Cambridge.

Phi Kappa Phi. 1966. *Animal Orientation and Navigation, 27th Annual Biology Colloquium, Oregon State University*. Oregon State University Press, Corvallis.

Rabaud, E. 1928. *How Animals Find Their Way About: A Study of Distant Orientation and Place-recognition*. International Library of Psychology, Philosophy & Scientific Method, London.

Roule, L. 1933. *Fishes, Their Journeys and Migrations*. W. W. Norton & Co., New York. (L)

Symposium in Garmisch-Partenkirchen. 1962. *Animal Orientation*. Advances in Biology, v. 26. Springer-Verlag, Berlin.

Williams, C. B. 1958. *Insect Migration*. Macmillan Co., New York.

    *F.   Central and peripheral neural mechanisms*

Adrian, E. D. (ed.). 1954. *Brain Mechanisms and Consciousness: A Symposium*. Blackwell Scientific Publications, Oxford.

Adrian, E. D. 1959. *Mechanisms of Nervous Action*. University of Pennsylvania Press, Philadelphia.

Andy, O. J., and H. Stephan. 1964. *The Septum of the Cat*. Charles C Thomas, Springfield, Ill.

Bajusz, E., and G. Jasmin (eds.). 1964. *Major Problems in Neuroendocrinology*. Williams & Wilkins Co., Baltimore, Md.

Beritoff, I. S. 1965. *Neural Mechanisms of Higher Vertebrate Behavior*. Little, Brown & Co., Boston, Mass.

Brazier, M. A. B. 1961. *Electrical Activity of the Nervous System*. Macmillan Co., New York.

Brazier, M. A. B. (ed.) 1961-63 *Brain and Behavior*, vols. 1 & 2 AIBS, Washington, D.C.

Bullock, T. H., and G. A. Horridge. 1965. *Structure and Function in the Nervous Systems of Invertebrates*, vols. 1 & 2. W. H. Freeman & Co., San Francisco, Calif.

Ciba Foundation. 1958. *Ciba Foundation Symposium on the Neurological Basis of Behavior*. J. & A. Churchill, London.

Delafresnaye, J. F. (ed.). 1961. *Brain Mechanisms and Learning: A Symposium*. Charles C Thomas, Springfield, Ill.

Diamond, S., R. S. Balvin, and F. R. Diamond. 1963. *Inhibition and Choice: A Neurobehavioral Approach to Problems of Plasticity in Behavior*. Harper & Row, Publishers, New York.

Etlinger, E. G. (ed.). 1965. *Functions of the Corpus Callosum*. Ciba Foundation Study Group no. 20. Little, Brown & Co., Boston, Mass.

Everett, N. B. 1965. *Functional Neuroanatomy, Including an Atlas of the Brain Stem*. 5th ed. Lea & Febiger, Philadelphia, Pa.

Field, J. (ed.). 1960. *Handbook of Physiology*. Sec. L, Neurophysiology. American Physiological Society, Washington, D.C.

Galambos, R. 1962. *Nerves and Muscles*. Doubleday & Co., Garden City, N.Y. (pa) (L)

Hebb, D. O. 1949. *The Organization of Behavior: A Neuropsychological Theory*. John Wiley & Sons, New York.

Herrick, C. J. 1962 (1924). *Neurological Foundations of Animal Behavior*. Hafner Publishing Co., New York.

Herrick, C. J. 1964 (1926). *Brains of Rats and Men: A Survey of the Origin and Biological Significance of the Cerebral Cortex*. Hafner Publishing Co., New York.

Hess, W. R. 1957. *The Functional Organization of the Diencephalon*. Grune & Stratton, New York.

Hess, W. R. 1964. *The Biology of Mind*. University of Chicago Press, Chicago, Ill.

Hodgkin, A. L. 1964. The Conduction of the Nervous Impulse. *The Sherrington Lectures*, no. 7. Charles C Thomas, Springfield, Ill.

Katz, B. 1966. *Nerve, Muscle and Synapse*. McGraw-Hill Book Co., New York.

Lashley, K. S. 1964 (1929). *Brain Mechanisms and Intelligence: A Quantitative Study of Injuries to the Brain*. Hafner Publishing Co., New York.

McCleary, R. A., and R. Y. Moore. 1965. *Subcortical Mechanisms of Behavior: The Psychological Functions of Primitive Parts of the Brain*. Basic Books, Inc., New York.

Otis, L. S., J. J. Bosley, and L. Birzis. 1960. Animal Research in Psychopharmocology: Central Nervous System Effects. Psychopharmacology Handbook, v. 2. *U.S. Public Health Service Publ. no. 1006*. U.S. Government Printing Office, Washington, D.C.

Pampiglione, G. 1963. *Development of Cerebral Function in the Dog*. Butterworth, Inc., Washington, D.C.

Pfeiffer, C. C., and J. R. Smythies (eds.). 1959—. *International Review of Neurobiology*. v. 1—. Academic Press, Inc, New York.

Purpura, D. P., and M. D. Yahr. 1966. *The Thalamus*. Columbia University Press, New York.

Roeder, K. D. 1963. *Nerve Cells and Insect Behavior*. Harvard University Press, Cambridge, Mass.

Scharrer, E., and B. Scharrer. 1963. *Neuroendocrinology*. Columbia University Press, New York.

Schmitt, F. O. (ed.). 1962. *Macromolecular Specificity and Biological Memory*. The M.I.T. Press, Cambridge, Mass.

Sevenster, P. 1961. *A Causal Analysis of a Displacement Activity (Fanning in Gasterosteus aculeatus L.)*. Behaviour, Supplement no. 9. E. J. Brill, Leiden.

Sherrington, C. S. 1961. *The Integrative Action of the Nervous System*. Yale University Press, New Haven, Conn.

Smith, D. D. 1965. *Mammalian Learning and Behavior*. W. B. Saunders Co., Philadelphia, Pa.

Treherne, J. E., and J. W. L. Beament (eds.). 1965. *Physiology of the Insect Central Nervous System: Papers from the 12th International Congress of Entomology, London, 1964.* Academic Press, Inc., New York.

Triggle, D. J. 1965. *Chemical Aspects of the Autonomic Nervous System.* Academic Press, Inc., New York.

Waelsch, H. (ed.). 1955. *Biochemistry of the Developing Nervous System.* Academic Press, Inc., New York.

Walsh, E. G. 1964. *Physiology of the Nervous System.* 2nd ed. Little, Brown & Co., Boston, Mass.

Welford, A. T., and J. E. Birren. 1965. *Behavior, Aging and the Nervous System.* Charles C Thomas, Springfield, Ill.

Wooldridge, D. E. 1963. *The Machinery of the Brain.* McGraw-Hill Book Co., New York. (pa) (L)

Young, J. Z. 1964. *A Model of the Brain.* Oxford University Press, Oxford.

## G. Reception and perception

Adrian, E. D. 1964 (1928). *The Basis of Sensation: The Action of the Sense Organs.* Hafner Publishing Co., New York.

Adrian, E. D. 1947. *The Physical Background of Perception.* Clarendon Press, Oxford.

Boyle, R. 1964. *Experiments and Considerations Touching Colour.* Academic Press, Inc., New York.

Case, J. 1966. *Sensory Mechanisms.* Macmillan Co., New York. (pa) (L)

Dethier, V. G. 1963. *The Physiology of Insect Senses.* John Wiley & Sons, New York.

Droscher, V. B. 1965. *The Mysterious Senses of Animals.* E. P. Dutton & Co., New York. (L)

Fox, S. S. 1960. *Sensory Deprivation and Maintained Sensory Input in Monkeys: A Behavioral and Neuro-pharmacological Study.* University of Michigan Press, Ann Arbor.

Frisch, K. von. 1950. *Bees: Their Vision, Chemical Senses and Language.* Cornell University Press, Ithaca, N.Y. (pa) (L)

Granit, R. 1955. *Receptors and Sensory Perception.* Yale University Press, New Haven, Conn.

Kare, M. R., and B. P. Halpern. 1961. *Physiological and Behavioral Aspects of Taste.* University of Chicago Press, Chicago, Ill.

Kellogg, W. N. 1961. *Porpoises and Sonar.* University of Chicago Press, Chicago, Ill.

Matthews, L. H., and M. Knight. 1963. *The Senses of Animals.* Museum Press, London. (L)

Milne, L. J., and M. J. Milne. 1962. *The Senses of Animals and Men.* Atheneum Publishers, New York.

Neff, W. D. (ed.). 1965. *Contributions to Sensory Physiology,* v. 1. Academic Press, Inc., New York.

Raskin, E. 1964. *Watchers, Pursuers and Masqueraders: Animals and Their Vision.* McGraw-Hill Book Co., New York. (L)

Smythe, R. H. 1961. *Animal Vision: What Animals See*. Charles C Thomas, Springfield, Ill. (L)

Society for Experimental Biology. 1962. *Biological Receptor Mechanisms*. Symposia no. 16. Cambridge University Press, New York.

Sutherland, N. S. 1962. *The Methods and Findings of Experiments on the Visual Discrimination of Shape by Animals*. Monograph no. 1, Experimental Psychology Society. Heffer, Cambridge.

Walls, G. L. 1963 (1942). *The Vertebrate Eye*. Hafner Publishing Co., New York.

Wright, R. H. 1964. *The Science of Smell*. G. Allen & Unwin, London.

Zoological Society of London. 1960. *Sensory Specialization in Response to Environmental Demands*. Symposia no. 3. Academic Press, Inc., New York. (pa)

Zotterman, Y. (ed.). 1963. *Olfaction and Taste: Proceedings of the First International Symposium Held at the Wenner-Gren Center, Stockholm, September 1962*. Pergamon Press, New York.

### H.   Physiological (including endocrine) mechanisms in behavior

Asdell, S. A. 1964. *Patterns of Mammalian Reproduction*. Cornell University Press, Ithaca, N.Y.

Beach, F. A. 1961 (1948). *Hormones and Behavior: A Survey of Interrelationships Between Endocrine Secretions and Patterns of Overt Response*. Cooper Square Publishers, New York.

Beach, F. A. 1965. *Sex and Behavior*. John Wiley & Sons, New York.

Beament, J. W. L., J. E. Treherne, and V. B. Wigglesworth (eds.). 1964. *Advances in Insect Physiology*, v. 2 Academic Press, Inc., New York.

Bullough, W. S. 1961. *Vertebrate Reproductive Cycles*. 2nd ed. John Wiley & Sons, New York.

Child, C. M. 1964. *Physiological Foundations of Behavior*. Hafner Publishing Co., New York.

Cloudsley-Thompson, J. L. 1961. *Rhythmic Activity in Animal Physiology and Behaviour*. Academic Press, Inc., New York.

Cloudsley-Thompson, J. L. 1963. *Biological Clocks*. Cold Spring Harbor Symp. Quant. Biol., v. 25.

Cole, H. H., and P. T. Cupps (eds.). 1959 *Reproduction in Domestic Animals*. Academic Press, Inc., New York.

Eiduson, S., E. Geller, A. Yuwiler, and B. T. Eiduson. 1964. *Biochemistry and Behavior*. D. Van Nostrand Co., Princeton, N.J.

Euler, U. S. von, and H. Heller (eds.). 1963. *Comparative Endocrinology*. V. 1, *Glandular Hormones;* v. 2, *Invertebrate Hormones—Tissue Hormones*. Academic Press, Inc., New York.

Gorbman, A. (ed.). 1959. *Comparative Endocrinology: Proceedings of Columbia University Symposium on Comparative Endocrinology, Cold Spring Harbor, New York, 1958*. John Wiley & Sons, New York.

Hafez, E. S. E. (ed.). 1962. *Reproduction in Farm Animals*. Lea & Febiger, Philadelphia, Pa.

Harker, J. E. 1964. *The Physiology of Diurnal Rhythms*. Cambridge University Press, Cambridge.

Harlow, H. F., and C. N. Woolsey (eds.). 1958. *Biological and Biochemical Bases of Behavior*. University of Wisconsin Press, Madison.

Hisaw, F. H., Jr. (ed.). 1963. *Physiology of Reproduction: Proceedings of the 22nd Biology Colloquium, 1961*. Oregon State University Press, Corvallis.

Jenkin, P. M. 1962. *Animal Hormones: A Comparative Survey. Part 1, Kinetic and Metabolic Hormones*. Pergamon Press, New York.

Mayer, W. V., and R. G. Van Gelder. 1963-65. *Physiological Mammalogy*. V. 1, Mammalian Populations; v. 2, Mammalian Reactions to Stressful Environments. Academic Press, Inc., New York.

McGuigan, F. J. 1963. *Biological Basis of Behavior: A Program*. Prentice-Hall, Englewood Cliffs, N.J.

Money, J. (ed.). 1965. *Sex Research: New Developments*. Holt, Rinehart and Winston, New York.

Morgan, C. 1965. *Physiological Psychology*. 3rd ed. McGraw-Hill Book Co., New York.

Pincus, G., K. V. Thiman, and E. R. Astwood (eds.). 1948-64. *The Hormones: Physiology, Chemistry and Applications*, vols. 1-5. Academic Press, Inc., New York.

Rockstein, M. (ed.). 1965. *The Physiology of Insecta*. V. 2, *The Insect and the External Environment*. Academic Press, Inc., New York.

Society for Experimental Biology. 1950. *Physiological Mechanisms in Animal Behaviour*. Symposia no. 4. Cambridge University Press, New York.

Steinbert, H., A. V. S. DeReuck, and J. Knight (eds.). 1964. *Animal Behaviour and Drug Action*. Little, Brown & Co., Boston, Mass.

Uhr, L., and J. G. Miller (eds.). 1960. *Drugs and Behavior*. John Wiley & Sons, New York.

Wilber, C. G. (ed.). 1964. *Handbook of Physiology*. Sec. 4, *Adaptation to the Environment*. Williams & Wilkins Co., Baltimore, Md.

Young, W. C. 1961. *Sex and Internal Secretions*, 3rd ed. (2 vols.). Williams & Wilkins Co., Baltimore, Md.

Zoological Society of London. 1960. *Cyclical Activity in Endocrine Systems*. Symposia no. 2. E. J. W. Barrington, London.

### I. Behavior genetics

Burns, M. 1952. *The Genetics of the Dog*. Tech. Commun. no. 9. Commonwealth Bureau of Animal Breeding and Genetics, Edinburgh.

Fuller, J. L., and W. R. Thompson. 1960. *Behavior Genetics*. John Wiley & Sons, New York.

Hutt, F. B. 1949. *The Genetics of the Fowl*. McGraw-Hill Book Co., New York.

Kallman, F. J. (ed.). 1962. *Expanding Goals of Genetics in Psychiatry*. Grune & Stratton, Inc., New York.

Lerner, I. M. 1958. *The Gentic Basis of Selection*. John Wiley & Sons, New York.

Munn, N. L. 1938. *Psychological Development: An Introduction to Genetic Psychology.* Houghton Mifflin Co., Boston.

Scott, J. P., and J. L. Fuller. 1965. *Genetics and Social Behavior of the Dog.* University of Chicago Press, Chicago, Ill.

Stockard, C. R., O. D. Anderson, and W. T. James. 1942. *Genetic and Endocrine Basis for Differences in Form and Behavior.* Wistar Institute Press.

### J. Effector mechanisms

Gray, J. 1953. *How Animals Move.* Cambridge University Press, New York. (L)

Muybridge, E. 1957 (1887). *Animals in Motion.* Dover Publications, New York. (L)

Slukin, W. 1964. *Imprinting and Early Learning.* Aldine Publishing Co., Chicago, Ill.

Storer, J. H. 1948. *The Flight of Birds.* Bull. no. 28. Cranbrook Institute of Science, Bloomfield Hills, Mich.

Waring, H. 1963. *Color Change Mechanisms of Cold-blooded Vertebrates.* Academic Press, Inc., New York.

Zoological Society of London. 1962. *Vertebrate Locomotion.* Symposia no. 5. Academic Press, Inc., New York. (pa)

### K. Ontogeny of behavior

Bliss, E. L. (ed.). 1962. *Roots of Behavior: Genetics, Instinct and Socialization in Animal Behavior.* Harper & Row, Publishers, New York.

Fiske, D. W., and S. R. Maddi. 1961. *Functions of Varied Experience.* Dorsey Press, Homewood, Ill.

Foss, B. M. (ed.). 1963-65. *Determinants of Infant Behaviour,* vols. 2 and 3. *Tavistock Study Group.* Methuen & Co., London.

Kellogg, W. N., and L. A. Kellogg. 1933. *The Ape and the Child: A Study of Environmental Influence Upon Early Behavior.* McGraw-Hill Book Co., New York.

Kruijt, J. P. 1964. *Ontogeny of Social Behavior in Burmese Red Junglefowl.* Behaviour, Supplement no. 12. E. J. Brill, Leiden.

Krushinskii, L. V. 1962. *Animal Behavior: Its Normal and Abnormal Development.* Consultants' Bureau Enterprises, New York.

Nice, M. M. 1962. *Development of Behavior in Precocial Birds.* Linnaean Society, New York.

Pycraft, W. P. 1913. *The Infancy of Animals.* Holt, Rinehart and Winston, New York.

Scott, J. P. 1951. *Minutes of the Conference on the Effects of Early Experience on Mental Health.* R. B. Jackson Memorial Laboratory, Bar Harbor, Me.

Zoological Society of London. 1962. *Imprinting and Early Learning.* Symposia no. 8. Academic Press, Inc., New York. (pa)

### L.  Evolution and behavior

Barnett, S. A. 1958. *A Century of Darwin.* William Heinemann, London.
Bell, P. R. (ed.). 1959. *Darwin's Biological Works: Some Aspects Reconsidered.* Cambridge University Press, Cambridge.
Blair, W. F. (ed.). 1961. *Vertebrate Speciation.* University of Texas Press, Austin.
Collias, N. E., and E. C. Collias. 1964. Evolution of Nest-Building in the Weaverbirds (*Ploceidae*). *Univ. Calif. Publ. in Zool.,* no. 73. University of California Press, Berkeley.
Crook, J. H. 1964. *The Evolution of Social Organization and Visual Communication in the Weaver Birds (Ploceinae).* Behaviour, Supplement no. 10, E. J. Brill, Leiden.
Holmes, S. J. 1911. *The Evolution of Animal Intelligence.* Holt, Rinehart and Winston, New York.
Huxley, J. (ed.). 1958. *Evolution as a Process.* 2nd ed. G. Allen & Unwin, London.
Kendeigh, S. C. 1952. *Parental Care and Its Evolution in Birds.* University of Illinois Press, Urbana.
Lorenz, K. Z. 1965. *Evolution and Modification of Behavior.* University of Chicago Press, Chicago, Ill.
Mayr, E. 1963. *Animal Species and Evolution.* Harvard University Press, Cambridge, Mass.
Rensch, B. 1960. *Evolution Above the Species Level.* Columbia University Press, New York.
Roe, A., and G. G. Simpson (eds.). 1958. *Behavior and Evolution.* Yale University Press, New Haven, Conn.
Russell, E. S. 1945. *The Directiveness of Organic Activities.* Cambridge University Press, Cambridge.
Tax, S. (ed.). 1960. *Evolution After Darwin.* University of Chicago Press, Chicago, Ill.
Zoological Society of London. 1962. *Evolutionary Aspects of Animal Communication.* Symposia no. 8. Academic Press, Inc., New York. (pa)

### M.  Methodology and techniques

American Institute of Biological Sciences. 1965. *Statistical Aids for Biologists in Case of Circular Observations.* AIBS, Washington, D.C.
Appleyard, R. 1949. *Ducks: Breeding, Rearing and Management.* 4th ed. Poultry World, London.
Batschelet, E. 1965. *Statistical Methods for the Analysis of Problems in Animal Orientation and Certain Biological Rhythms.* AIBS, Washington, D.C.
Boosey, E. J. 1963. *Foreign Bird Keeping: A Complete Guide to Breeding and Management.* Iliffe & Sons, London.
Caceres, C. A. (ed.). 1965. *Biomedical Telemetry.* Academic Press, Inc., New York.

Crandall, L. S. 1964. *Management of Wild Mammals in Captivity*. University of Chicago Press, Chicago, Ill.

Edwards, A. L. 1954. *Statistical Methods for the Behavioral Sciences,* Holt, Rinehart and Winston, New York.

Farris, E. J. (ed.). 1950. *The Care and Breeding of Laboratory Animals*. John Wiley & Sons, New York.

Fisher, R. A. 1947. *The Design of Experiments*. 4th ed. Oliver and Boyd, Edinburgh.

Guilford, J. P. 1954. *Psychometric Methods*. 2nd ed. McGraw-Hill Book Co., New York.

Guilford, J. P. 1965. *Fundamental Statisitcs in Psychology and Education*. McGraw-Hill Book Co., New York.

Linton, D. 1964. *Photographing Nature*. Doubleday & Co., New York. (pa) (L)

Macfadyen, A. 1963. *Animal Ecology: Aims and Methods*. Pitman Publishing Corp., New York.

McGuigan, F. J. 1960. *Experimental Psychology: A Methodological Approach*. Prentice-Hall, Englewood Cliffs, N.J.

Mitchell, H. 1939. *Raising Game Birds*. Wm. Penn Publishing Corp. (now Tudor Publishing Corp., New York), Philadelphia, Pa.

Mosby, H. S. 1963. *Wildlife Investigational Techniques*. 2nd ed. The Wildlife Society, Washington, D.C.

Murry, W. E., and P. F. Salisbury (eds.). 1964. *Biomedical Sciences Instrumentation,* vol. 2. Plenum Press, Inc., New York.

Saunders, B. 1952. *Training You to Train Your Dog*. Rev. ed. Doubleday & Co., Garden City, New York.

Siegel, S. 1956. *Nonparametric Statistics for the Behavioral Sciences*. McGraw-Hill Book Co., New York.

Silvan, J. 1966. *Raising Laboratory Animals: A Handbook for Biological and Behavioral Research*. The Natural History Press (Doubleday & Co., Inc.), Garden City, N.Y. (pa) (L)

Slater, L. E. 1963. *Bio-telemetry; The Use of Telemetry in Animal Behavior and Physiology in Relation to Ecological Problems. Proceedings of Interdisciplinary Conference*. Pergamon Press, New York.

Snedigar, R. 1963. *Our Small Native Animals: Their Habits and Care*. Rev. and enlarged ed. Dover Publications, New York. (pa) (L)

II. PERIODICALS

*Animal Behaviour.*
*Behaviour: An International Journal of Comparative Ethology.*
*The Journal of Comparative and Physiological Psychology.*
*Zeitschrift für Tierpsychologie.*

In addition to the above, reports of ethological research appear in a number of zoological and ecological journals, including:

*Auk*
*Journal of Animal Ecology*
*Journal of Mammalogy*
*American Zoologist*
*Copeia*

# INDEX